HEPARIN

OXFORD MEDICAL PUBLICATIONS

HEPARIN

IN THE

TREATMENT OF THROMBOSIS

AN ACCOUNT OF ITS CHEMISTRY, PHYSIOLOGY AND APPLICATION IN MEDICINE

BY

J. ERIK JORPES, M.D.

Reader in biochemistry, The Çaroline Institute, Stockholm, Sweden

WITH A FOREWORD

BY

J. R. LEARMONTH, C. B. E., Ch. M., F. R. C. S. E.

Professor of surgery, University of Edinburgh

SECOND EDITION

GEOFFREY CUMBERLEGE

OXFORD UNIVERSITY PRESS, LONDON

NEW YORK, TORONTO

1946

OXFORD UNIVERSITY PRESS
PRESS ROAD, NEASDEN, N. W. 10
London Edinburgh Glasgow New York
Toronto Melbourne Cape Town Bombay
Calcutta Madras
GEOFFREY CUMBERLEGE
PUBLISHER TO THE UNIVERSITY

First Edition 1939
Second Edition 1946

PRINTED IN SWEDEN
BY HÅKAN OHLSSON, LUND

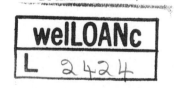

FOREWORD

By

J. R. Learmonth, C. B. E., Ch. M., F. R. C. S. E.

Regius Professor of Clinical Surgery and Professor of Surgery
in the University of Edinburgh

It was, I think, the elder Kocher who once remarked that
intellectual satisfaction in medicine was to be derived only
from a mastery of every aspect of one of its subjects. If
the dictum be true, then Dr Jorpes must have had ample
recompense for his labours in producing this monograph.
In its table of contents one may find every aspect, from
the detailed account of the chemistry of heparin (to which
the author's researches have contributed so much), to the
clinical and statistical records of its therapeutic applications. In addition, there are sections devoted to a similar
consideration of dicoumarol.

The discovery of these anticoagulant substances has provided an extensive field in pure research, as well as clinical
applications of great importance. So far as the former is
concerned, while perusal of the chapters on the chemistry
and biological properties of heparin and dicoumarol reveals
substantial and important observations, it is clear that there
is still work to be done, and it is within my knowledge that
Dr Jorpes and his co-workers are continuing their pro-
ductive activity in this field. The therapeutic applications
of anticoagulant substances have been developed from their
use in the more restricted fields of experimental physiology
and of blood analysis. Naturally the first application was
to the surgery of blood vessels, which had been hampered
by the tendency to thrombosis at suture lines. In peace, the
reconstructive surgery of blood vessels provides a small and,
it must be noted, a diminishing field; in war, this application of anticoagulant substances is governed by the tactical
considerations which limit facilities for the control of the

method in the laboratory. However, in peace, thrombo-embolic conditions constitute a group which in any country is substantial, and in Sweden, for some unexplained reason, is a formidable problem. It would appear, from the figures of Swedish workers, that both the immediate mortality associated with these conditions in their grave forms, and the continuing disabilities associated with the later com-plications of the less severe forms, have been brought under control as a result of the administration of heparin or dicou-marol to meet emergencies such as pulmonary embolism, to prevent the occurrence of embolism as a complication of thrombosis and finally to act prophylactically in prevent-ing thrombosis after operations. The statistical analysis of these three applications carries conviction; and I have recently had an opportunity of seeing the care and discri-mination with which these clinical studies have been made. There is no doubt in my mind that the methods described in the latter part of this monograph are a substantial con-tribution to the therapy of dangerous and crippling con-ditions.

The monograph is complete: there is here assembled, in a form readily available, an account of *every aspect* of a subject. The biochemist, the histologist, the haematologist and the clinician each will find in its pages the most recent work on his special interest, with comprehensive references. And the different aspects have been drawn together, critically examined and set out with clarity by one who is a master of his subject.

PREFACE TO THE SECOND EDITION

Since the publication of the first Heparin monograph in 1939, the progress made in the treatment of thrombosis and pulmonary embolism with heparin and the introduction of dicumarol have greatly increased the interest in thrombo-embolic diseases. Thrombosis can now be influenced to a degree which was unheard of a few years ago. The future use of heparin in thrombosis was at that time very cautiously assessed. Today we know that heparin is as specific in thrombosis as insulin is in diabetes. In a discussion of the possible anticoagulant substances, heparin, the physiological agent of the body, will always take first place. It has been found that careful attention to the initial signs of thrombosis and early treatment with heparin, in conjunction with active movements, will limit the growth of the thrombus and abort the disease. Consequently, it is evident that the main interest in heparin will in the future centre around its anticoagulant properties and that a discussion of heparin must also include the question of thrombosis and embolism.

In this edition, therefore, a fairly complete account is given of the recent experience in the use of heparin in thrombosis and embolism.

Since the discovery of the specific anticoagulants will shortly result in a complete change in the medical and social aspects of the thrombo-embolic diseases, attention has also been paid to their social importance.

J. Erik Jorpes

PREFACE TO THE FIRST EDITION

The author has felt that the recent developments in connection with heparin make it desirable to assemble the more essential features of our present knowledge of the substance into a form easily available for physiologists and physicians. A few years ago heparin was a substance the physiological significance of which was altogether too uncertain to attract any great amount of interest. In physiological and clinical laboratories it found a certain application as a unique natural anticoagulant. The research of the last few years has thrown so much light on this field that both the physiological significance and the clinical applicability of heparin can now be discussed against a different background.

Combined physiological and chemical research has led to a satisfactory solution of an important physiological problem. It has been possible to show that the substance in question in all probability contributes towards maintaining the fluidity of the blood and of certain body fluids. For this purpose it has the particularly suitable chemical structure of a polysaccharide of high molecular weight, with an unusually high content of ester sulphates, up to 40 per cent sulphuric acid in the strongest preparations.

Even before this was known, physiologists had found that the most effective coagulation-inhibiting substances had a similar composition, consisting of strong acids with a high molecular weight. The knowledge of the chemical nature of this substance and of its precipitation and staining reactions has now made it possible to demonstrate heparin in its natural *milieu* in the body. This has brought to light the interesting fact that the substance is produced by a type of cell which histologists have long recognized to be located in the immediate neighbourhood of the blood-vessels as well as in their walls. This finding is of extreme importance in connection with the discussion of the physiology of heparin.

With this background it does not seem unjustifiable to regard heparin as a hormone. Even if it is not a stimulating agent in the original sense of Bayliss and Starling, nevertheless it is produced by a specific type of cell and is secreted into the blood and tissue fluids where it contributes towards a maintenance of their physical properties.

The accumulated experience now available has also made it possible to prepare the substance in pure form so that its clinical applicability can be tested out. In this connection heparin has already lived up to many of the expectations in regard to it. As a physiological anticoagulant it facilitates all sorts of operative procedures on experimental animals, and makes it possible to obtain native blood for as different purposes as transfusion and ordinary morphological and chemical analysis. Since the substance has been available in pure form it has been possible to take up the most important associated problem, namely, whether administration of an excess of heparin directly into the blood can help to prevent undesired coagulation as in the formation of a thrombus. The experience already available clearly shows that heparin is of value as well in the prevention as for the treatment of thrombosis. Given post-operatively in surgical cases it seems to favourably counteract the formation of initial thrombi. In a series of cases of acute thrombosis in the central vein of the retina heparinization of the patient has resulted in recovery and restoration of vision, a course which is unusual in this disease. Thereby evidence is obtained that heparinization must be useful in other cases of thrombosis in man as well. As great medical interest is attached to this problem, it would give particular satisfaction to the theoretical branches of medicine if the expectations in this field could to some extent be realized. The physiologist, biochemist, and physician have here a common interest, for heparin has passed from pure physiology to medicine by way of biochemistry, thus following the pathway of so many of the most important therapeutic discoveries of the present day.

An attempt has been made to follow the historical development in this field partly because it has been very typical of so many advances in medicine and partly in order to honour William H. Howell, the discoverer of heparin, at a time when his pioneer work promises to be of value not only to physiology but to medicine in general. He is an eminent representative of the series of successful scientists who have advanced America's physiology and medicine to a leading position.

J. E. Jorpes

Contents

PART II.

HEPARIN AND THROMBOSIS

LIST OF ILLUSTRATIONS

PART I

The Chemistry and Physiology
of Heparin

CHAPTER I

The Discovery and Chemistry of Heparin.

The Discovery of Heparin.

As is common in biology, the discovery of heparin was incidental. One of William H. Howell's collaborators, Jay McLean,[1] was in 1916 assigned the task of purifying the phosphatide cephalin. Howell himself had earlier found that this lipoid exerted such a strong thromboplastic action that it seemed to be the activator, thrombokinase, which induces coagulation of the blood.

It then became of fundamental importance to know whether the thromboplastic effect was inherent in pure cephalin or due to adherent impurities. Cephalin was therefore prepared from the brain and other organs and submitted to thorough purification. It still exerted a very strong accelerating effect upon the coagulation of the blood.

Simultaneously two other "phosphatides", at that time believed to be individual compounds, were prepared by McLean. These were the heart phosphatide cuorin, previously described by Erlandsen, and the liver phosphatide of Baskoff. They were separated from cephalin by means of their insolubility in boiling alcohol. However, contrary to expectation, these alleged phosphatides retarded the course of coagulation to quite a considerable degree.

McLean describes his discovery as follows:

"The cuorin, on the contrary when purified by repeated precipitation in alcohol at 60° C., has no thromboplastic effect — indeed it possesses an anticoagulating power as may be illustrated by the following experiment.

---

[1] A second-year medical student at Johns Hopkins University.

Dog's oxalated plasma and dog's serum

Using-Plasma, 8 drops; phosphatid, 3 drops; serum, 3 drops.
Control-Plasma, 8 drops; water, 3 drops; serum, 3 drops.
Heart cephalin solid clot 3 min.
Cuorin not clotted in 6 hours.
Control sliding clot in 9 min.

Cuorin added to blood fresh from the artery will delay its coagulation remarkably. These two phosphatids from the heart have practically the same solubilities, they pass through repeated processes of extraction together and in the final stages are only separated from each other by the solution of the cephalin in alcohol at 60° C. It is unlikely that an impurity would adhere to one of these phosphatids and not to the other.

The heparphosphatide on the other hand, when purified by many precipitations in alcohol at 60° C., has no thromboplastic action, showing on the contrary a marked power to inhibit the coagulation. The anticoagulating action of this phosphatid is being studied and will be reported upon later.''

This finding was worthy of attention because no anticoagulant substance had previously been found in the mammalian tissues. Therefore Howell, who was an authority in the field of blood coagulation, paid due attention in his further work on coagulation to this finding of McLean. In a Harvey Lecture, on April 7, 1917 he gave an account of the result of the first year's work. The active substance or substances prevented coagulation of the blood *in vitro* and *in vivo* if present in sufficient concentration. One milligram of the substance inhibited coagulation for 24 hours in 1 to 2 ml. of blood kept at 0° C. The blood of dogs would not clot after the intravenous injection of 100 mg. of the substance per kilo of body-weight. Injection into animals was not followed by any rise in blood-pressure or any alteration in the frequency of the pulse or respiration. Using the ordinary methods for the isolation of phosphatides, the active substance was obtained most easily from liver but also from other tissues such as heart, muscle, lymph nodes, and even the uterine mucous membrane. Howell found that the inhibition of the coagulation process took place during the first phase so that the prothrombin in the circulating blood did not become activated. He believed that this natural antiprothrombin had a general distribution throughout the body.

The last sentences of his lecture on the coagulation of the blood were devoted by Howell to this new anticoagulant substance recently discovered in his laboratory. His conclusions are of particular interest today, thirty years later, when his cautious prophecy about the possible future use of this antiprothrombin in "the therapeutic treatment of disorders of coagulation" has been fulfilled.

On this occasion Howell made the following statement about the possible future use in medicine of cephalin and antiprothrombin:

"In conclusion attention may be called briefly to the fact that we have now some knowledge concerning two substances, both belonging to the group of phosphatids which influence the clotting of blood in opposite ways, one, cephalin, causing an acceleration, the other, antiprothrombin, a retardation. Neither of these substances apparently provokes an injurious reaction in the living animal, and we may hope therefore that they will find a suitable application in experimental work and possibly in the therapeutic treatment of disorders of coagulation."

In 1918 Howell and Holt described in more detail the characteristics of this substance and, because of its abundant occurrence in the liver, named it heparin. In 1922 and 1924 Howell improved the method of preparation, and in 1928 he submitted a detailed report on its chemistry and physiology. It did not seem improbable to him that this substance might be of physiological significance, and in the discussion on coagulation of the blood heparin was referred to as a physiological anticoagulant.

The Schmidt-Fuld-Morawitz theory of coagulation.

Clotting of the blood is an extremely expedient procedure. In the event of a minor trauma to smaller blood vessels, the leakage can be stopped by conversion of the blood at the site of the injury into a solid phase. The same process takes place in drawn blood. Although the plasma contains about 8 per cent of protein, there is only 0.1 to 0.2 per cent of fibrinogen, the precursor of fibrin. None the less it suffices to give the entire mass of blood a solid form. The mechanism of the actual clotting is extremely complicated, and we are acquainted with only a few of the fundamental facts. For our knowledge of these we are in the first place indebted to Professor Alexander Schmidt, of Dorpat. His papers from 1861 to 1895 stand in a class by themselves. As far as thoroughness is concerned, the only investigations of his contemporaries which reach the same standard are those of Olof Hammarsten (1899) on the activation of the coagulation system with calcium.

According to Schmidt, the conversion of fibrinogen to fibrin was due to an enzyme which he named thrombin. His assumption was based on the observation of earlier workers that hydrocele fluid and exudates containing fibrinogen could be made to coagulate if they were mixed with serum in which the active ferment was present. Blood plasma, however, did not contain this substance but, instead, its precursor, the so-called prothrombin. Schmidt supposed that the activation was brought about by 'a zymoplastic substance', secreted by the white blood-cells which split thrombin from prothrombin. Posterity agrees with him that an activator, which Morawitz later called thrombokinase and American authors thromboplastin, brings about the conversion of prothrombin to thrombin. The enzymatic activity of the latter is also evident. It is probable that it denatures the fibrinogen in a manner similar to that of chymosin in the curdling of milk.

Our knowledge of the activator thrombokinase or thromboplastin is very limited. As it gives rise to the formation of thrombin, and thereby leads to clotting, it occupies a central position in the mechanism of coagulation.

The coagulation theory of Schmidt has been supplemented by Spiro and Fuld (1904) and by Morawitz (1904 a and b).

The plasma of the fluid blood is rich in prothrombin but cannot contain free kinase, which is present in quantities in the tissue as well as in the walls of the blood vessels. Tissues

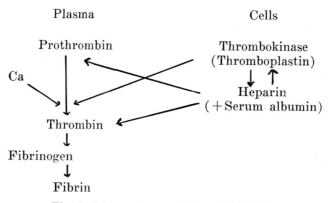

Fig. 1. Scheme of coagulation of the blood.

such as brain, testis, and muscle are unusually rich in kinase, which is most profuse in the blood-platelets, hence the term thrombocytes. Mechanical or chemical trauma, which cause platelet disintegration, release kinase into the plasma, thus providing the first prerequisite for coagulation. It is also believed that kinase is released from the vessel walls and muscle tissues when they are injured. This is the basis of the rapid coagulation when blood comes in contact with injured muscle.

The thrombocytes are one of the formed elements of the blood. In man there are from 200,000 to 300,000 per cubic millimetre of blood. They play a decisive rôle in the formation of a thrombus. A large part of the initial thrombus is composed of accumulations of thrombocytes. Mechanical or possibly even chemical injury to the vessels causes the thrombocytes to agglutinate in clumps and to disintegrate with liberation of kinase locally, so that thrombi form along the vessel walls.

The discovery of heparin introduced a new factor into the discussion of coagulation. The marked capacity of this substance to block prothrombin, plus its natural occurrence in the organism, led to the assumption that it was a physiological anticoagulant, an antiprothrombin. Howell suggested that heparin possibly blocked prothrombin and prevented its activation. When kinase was produced it neutralized heparin, and the released prothrombin could be activated. At an early stage he believed that this activation was taken care of by the calcium ions. Later it was agreed that it is kinase which in the presence of these ions activates the prothrombin. It seemed to Howell very plausible to assume that heparin plays a physiological rôle. According to Schmidt, Fuld and Morawitz it is only the entrance of kinase which determines when the blood will pass from a fluid to a solid phase, and for this only an injury to the thrombocytes is necessary. In consideration of their lability, the system had to be regarded as deficient in protective mechanisms. The heparin could counteract undesired coagulation by taking care of small quantities of thrombokinase.

The development of our knowledge of the chemistry of heparin.

The Work of Howell.

In 1924 Howell corrected his original assumption that the active principle in the acetone precipitate was a phosphatide. The substance turned out to be free from phosphorus and to contain sugar.

It may be of interest to mention that the cuorin of Erlandsen and the hepar-phosphatide of Baskoff were later shown to be mixtures of cephalin and its disintegration products.

According to Howell's improved 1922 method for the preparation of heparin, dog liver was rinsed free of blood, cut in pieces, and dried in the air. The dry powder was boiled in methyl alcohol and the residue extracted with physiological salt solution. The active substance was precipitated from the extract with an equal volume of acetone. One milligram of the preparation so obtained prevented coagulation in 5 ml. of cat blood at 0° for 24 hours. To purify the preparation the glycogen was removed by digestion with Taka-diastase. Proteins were removed with a 10 per cent solution of cadmium chloride. From then on the preparation was stronger than hirudin and 1 mg. prevented coagulation in 40 ml. of cat blood. The preparation now (1924) contained 2.7 per cent of nitrogen and gave a positive Molisch reaction as evidence of the presence of carbohydrate. It was reported to be free from sulphur.

A comprehensive paper in 1928 presented the chemistry and properties of heparin. One milligram now prevented coagulation in 100 ml. of cat blood for 24 hours at 0° C. In the process of purification, inactive material had been removed with an aluminium silicate (Lloyd's reagent) and the active substance had been purified by precipitation with an excess of barium hydroxide solution, both being principles which later came into use in the purification of heparin.

Careful analysis of this preparation revealed only that it contained uronic acid, as evidenced by the characteristic colour reaction with naphthoresorcinol and hydrochloric acid.

In addition to this observation, still another finding of Howell should be mentioned, because it demonstrates the thoroughness with which he worked. When the substance was hydrolysed with hydrochloric and nitric acid respectively, for the furfurol and mucic acid tests, there was precipitated in both instances a small quantity of crystals which on analysis turned out to be calcium sulphate. No comments were made, and the impression is left that this was a question of contamination with inorganic material, especially as the preparation had previously (1924) been described as free from sulphur.

The properties of heparin were described in detail by Howell. It was thermostabile and relatively insensitive to the action of bacteria. It was resistant to most common enzymes such as maltase, emulsin, Taka-diastase, and proteases. Like other polysaccharides it was not precipitated from aqueous solution by the ordinary metal salts, except basic lead acetate. It was, however, precipitated by barium chloride in excess and by barium hydroxide.

A practical result of Howell's investigations was the commercial production of heparin, for experimental purposes, by the Hynson, Westcott & Dunning Co. of Baltimore as early as 1922.

The Investigations of the Connaught Laboratories at the University of Toronto, Canada.

Because of the importance of heparin in experimental and clinical physiology, the Connaught Laboratories under the direction of Best, have devoted a great deal of attention to this substance.

Charles and Scott, the latter author known for his excellent work on the crystallization of insulin and the effect of zinc on its action, elaborated in 1933 a method of preparing heparin, which owing to a novel principle of extraction gave a greatly increased yield.

The ground-up fresh ox liver is extracted with weak alkali either directly or preferably after autolysis at 37° C. for 24 hours. The mass is extracted for 1 hour with 0.5 N NaOH containing ammonium sulphate, after which it is coagulated by heating to 70° C. The filtered extract is acidified to pH 2 which precipitates the heparin along with protein. After removal of ammonium sulphate with water the fat is removed with alcohol. The precipitate is dissolved and digested with trypsin for 36 hours. Proteins not broken down and the heparin are precipitated with alcohol from the acid solution. The final purification is performed with Lloyd's reagent, with cadmium chloride and by fractional precipitation with acetone.

In the preparation of heparin from the lungs, Charles, Scott, and Fischer (1934) could isolate at a certain stage a so-called antiheparin with marked thromboplastic action. In contrast to heparin this substance was alcohol soluble like other kinase preparations.

This new principle of extracting heparin from fresh organs as introduced by Charles and Scott proved to be of extraordinary value for the further development of this field. Thanks to the greater yield of heparin the substance became available for chemical analysis and even later for clinical experiments.

The Toronto researchers furthermore made the interesting observation that heparin occurs not only in the liver but also in other organs and was especially abundant in the lungs. As early as 1916 Howell had obtained a heparin effect with preparations from lymph nodes, heart and muscle, but apart from this observation there had been reason to believe that the liver was the source of the substance. The Toronto workers proved, however, that heparin has a general distribution throughout the body. The question of its physiological significance thus became still more accentuated.

The purest heparin preparations obtained by these workers contained 25—33 per cent of ash and about 2 per cent of nitrogen. Contrary to all expectations Charles and Scott did make some findings which were not in agreement with Howell's observations of 1928. Thus Howell had not found nitrogen in his purest preparations, and his positive naphthoresorcinol reaction was negative on their preparations. This led them to draw very cautious conclusions, and they left the question of the chemical nature of heparin entirely open (1933).

Albert Fischer and his collaborator A. Schmitz at the Biological Institute of the Carlsberg Foundation, Copenhagen, in 1933 worked out a method with which they believed they had obtained pure heparin, a brucine salt of which was reported to be crystalline. Heparin was stated by them to be a nitrogen-free polysaccharide, containing acidic groups and having the composition $C_{18}H_{32}O_{17}$ · · 6 H$_2$O.

A survey of these various findings provides no uniform conception of the chemical nature of heparin. The only certain fact was the carbohydrate content of the preparations.

The Investigations at the Caroline Institute, Stockholm.

As Howell's observation in regard to the reaction for uronic acids seemed convincing, the interest of the present author was first directed toward this question. Heparin preparations obtained from ox and horse liver were analysed in 1935 (Jorpes 1935 b) for uronic acids according to Tollens-Lefèvre. The material was hydrolysed with hydrochloric acid, and the carbon dioxide liberated from the uronic acid was collected in the usual way in barium hydroxide or on ascarite in a Pregl-tube. This principle of analysis is more reliable than the naphthoresorcinol reaction and has the advantage of providing a quantitative estimation of the uronic acid content. On hydrolysis carbon dioxide developed in such quantities that a uronic acid could be assumed to be present, a finding which was in agreement with that of Howell.

It was valuable to find that during the purification the uronic acid content rose with increasing activity of the preparations. Fortunately, research in carbohydrate chemistry had at that time given us methods by means of which even small amounts of uronic acids could be determined quantitatively.

The second component discovered was a hexosamine. In this case also our knowledge allowed us to get information, which could not be obtained at the time Howell did his work. A colour reaction, worked out by Zuckerkandl and Klebermass in 1931, permitted the demonstration of very small amounts of hexosamine. As modified by Elson and Morgan in 1933, the reaction could be applied for quantitative purposes. It was now possible to prove that the heparin preparations contained one molecule of amino sugar for each molecule of uronic acid. The occurrence of a hexosamine also explained the nitrogen content in the preparations of Charles and Scott. With the Lassaigne reaction used by Howell, as small an amount as 2 per cent of nitrogen can easily be overlooked.

A survey of these findings revealed that from 90 to 95 per cent of the purified heparin consisted of known components (Tables I and II). The preparations contained about 40 per cent of ash in the air-dry substance. The hexosamine and the uronic acid together also made up 40 per cent, and we still counted on the presence of acetic acid in the molecule because according to Fürth and collaborators (1934), all amino sugars in nature are monoacetylated. This is the case with the chondroitin sulphuric acid, the chitin, the immuno-polysaccharides of pneumococci and with the blood group substance A.

The key to the problem, the analysis of the ash. The organic substance thus resembled chondroitin. An analysis of the ash showed that it also contained sulphuric acid, the similarity to chondroitin sulphuric acid thus being quite evident. This compound, however, is completely devoid of anticoagulant activity. As the samples seemed to consist of chondroitin sulphuric acid and ash exclusively, the problem was at this stage as puzzling as ever. The quantitative analysis of the ash making up 25—40 per cent of the preparations led to the complete solution of the question.

It has already been mentioned that Howell found that

TABLE I

Analyses for Nitrogen and Uronic Acid in Purified Heparin Preparations

Percentage of air-dry substance

Preparation	1	2	3	4
Carbon dioxide (Tollens-Lefèvre)	..	4.60	..	..
	..	4.27	..	..
	3.92	4.16	4.11	3.99
	3.89	4.16	4.05	4.04
Average	3.91	4.30	4.08	4.02
Nitrogen (Kjeldahl)	1.63	1.91	1.65	1.64

TABLE II

The Composition of the Preparations analysed in Table I

Percentage of air-dry substance

Preparation	1	2	3	4
Moisture	15.60	13.90	13.84	10.90
Ash	38.40	40.80	41.09	45.15
Hexuronic acid (found)	17.26	18.98	18.00	17.74
Hexosamine less H_2O (calculated 1 mol. per mol. uronic acid)........	14.32	15.74	14.93	14.71
Acetic acid less H_2O (calculated 1 mol. per mol. uronic acid)	3.74	4.11	3.89	3.83
Maximum amount of protein calc. from the N content..............	2.41	3.38	2.19	3.06
	91.73	96.91	93.94	95.39

the ash contained calcium sulphate. His followers all neglected the ash, as is commonly the case. An analysis of our preparations proved that the ash consisted of magnesium and calcium sulphate. The first important question was, what percentage of the sulphates in the ash belonged to the supposed chondroitin sulphuric acid? To ascertain this the free sulphates were precipitated in acid solution with barium chloride. Only a small part of the sulphates was directly precipitable. The fraction precipitable after hydrolysis with mineral acid, thus consisting of ester sulphates, was on the contrary very much larger than expected, corresponding to 7—8 per cent of ester-bound sulphur in the samples. This finding was indeed surprising. In this case a chondroitin sulphuric acid would contain only about 3 per cent of sulphur. By means of dialysis through a parchment membrane it could be proved that the sulphur did not occur in free sulphates. After hydrolysis with concentrated or 20 per cent hydrochloric acid all the sulphur could be precipitated with barium chloride. The heparin could therefore be considered to contain a large amount of ester sulphates.

This being the case, one detail in the earlier literature, which previously had been rather confusing, could easily be explained. Howell as well as Charles and Scott had found at least 25 per cent of ash in their purest preparations, rather surprising for a polysaccharide. Howell's finding (1928) that calcium sulphate crystallized when heparin was subjected to acid hydrolysis, was an indication which might easily have led him to the correct solution of the question. The ash of the preparations of all the earlier writers thus contained non-volatile alkaline sulphates.

This fact was also demonstrated by A. Fischer. He expressed the view that heparin combines with neutral salts 'in lockerer molekularer Bindung' by means of some kind of co-valences. Even the crystalline brucine salt contained ash, thus demonstrating the difficulty of completely removing the alkali and replacing it with brucine.

It should be mentioned, too, that the presence of sulphates and calcium was observed by the routine analyst of Schering-Kahlbaum.[1]

Here is an example of what has happened in connection with the discovery of many important biological substances in the past, namely, that an essential element has been overlooked for decades. Thus Liebig himself, who introduced elementary analysis into organic chemistry, remained ignorant of the phosphorus content of the inosinic acid, discovered and analyzed by himself in 1847. In 1895

---

[1] In a personal communication to the author Professor Howell informed him that Dr. Dunning of Baltimore made similar observations about the sulphur content of the earlier heparin preparations.

Haiser discovered the high phosphorus content and the close relationship between the inosinic acid and the nucleic acids. Furthermore the sulphur content of taurin was for a long time overlooked, two atoms of oxygen being written in the formula instead of the sulphur atom.

The analysis of the ash thus threw additional light on the field and elucidated many obscure points in the earlier literature. Another detail in the chemical nature of heparin, the uncommonly strong resistance of this polysaccharide to acid hydrolysis, has caused equally great confusion and will be discussed later.

These findings appeared to clear up the chemical structure of heparin. The samples seemed to consist of a polysulphuric ester of chondroitin. Later, when the amino sugar was found to be glucosamine and not galactosamine (Jorpes and Bergström 1936), the name had to be changed to mucoitin and the preparations to be considered as polysulphuric esters of mucoitin.[1] It is quite evident that the quantitative analysis reproduced in Table II leaves very little room for any further substances or contaminants in these preparations.

The Chemical Composition of Heparin.

As is evident from Table II the organic skeleton of the heparin preparations is built up of an acetylated amino sugar and a uronic acid. The disaccharide unit seems to be the same as in the mucoitin sulphuric acid of Levene and the hyaluronic acid of K. H. Meyer. Meyer himself, in collaboration with Smyth, was able in 1938 to confirm this view concerning the chemical nature of heparin. His quantitative analysis of nitrogen, amino sugar, uronic acid, acetyl content, sulphur and ash gave figures very close to the ones calculated for a polysulphuric ester of mucoitin. Identical figures except for the acetyl content were found by Wolfrom, Weisblat, Karabinos, McNeely and McLean (1943). Later, different authors have agreed that heparin belongs to the

---

[1] Here the assumption was made that the hexuronic acid is glucuronic acid. This was also later proved to be the case (Wolfrom and Rice 1946).

same group of substances as chondroitin sulphuric acid (Reinert and Winterstein 1939 and Charles and Todd 1940). The amino sugar is glucosamine in the heparin from the liver as well as in that from the lung. The uronic acid has recently been identified by Wolfrom and Rice (1946) as glucuronic acid.

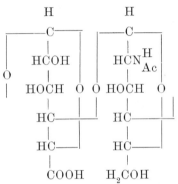

Fig. 2. The disaccharide unit of heparin (internal linkages unknown).

Because of the various analytical results the question of the acetyl content of heparin has been amply discussed. Thus Charles and Todd (1940) found figures varying from 1.2 to 2.9 per cent depending on the analytical technique applied. Wolfrom, Weisblat, Karabinos, McNeely and Mc Lean (1943) found no acetyl groups at all in crystalline barium salts although the NH_2 group of the amino sugar was not free. With 20 per cent toluene sulphonic acid as used by these authors no acetic acid was liberated. The same observation was made by Jorpes and Bergström in 1937, who found that if heparin is hydrolysed with 10 volume per cent of sulphuric acid for 3 hours at 100° C, a considerable amount of acetic acid is liberated. The extraordinary resistance of the heparin polysaccharide to hydrolytic agents makes such drastic treatment necessary in this case, even though related substances easily give up their acetyl group with the ordinary analytical procedures.

The protein-free samples of heparin contained about 10 per cent of sulphur (calculated on dry substance), *present in the ester sulphates.* At first there arose the difficulty of locating these sulphate groups in the molecule, because about $2\,^1/_2$ sulphate groups corresponded to each mucoitin complex, which did not seem very probable. The question was simplified when it could be demonstrated that the preparations were not homogenous; this was possible with the aid of brucine. For that purpose the alkali was removed by electrodialysis and the free acid remaining in the inner cell was neutralized with brucine. The brucine salt obtained could be dissolved and fractionated in water, the solubility of the fractions decreasing with the increasing content of sulphur. The fraction with the highest sulphur content was soluble only in a large volume of boiling water. After removing the brucine, the calcium salt of this fraction contained an amount of sulphur which very closely corresponded to the composition of a mucoitin trisulphuric acid. It was thus possible to consider the original preparations as being mixtures of mucoitin disulphuric and trisulphuric acids.

TABLE III

Heparin Fractions Recovered from Brucine Salts

Substance recovered from	Air-dried substance	Per cent of dry substance			CO_2	Uronic acid	Hexosamine (Elson and Morgan method)		S per molecule uronic acid	Heparin activity
		Ash	S	N			Found	Calculated		
Mother liquor 1st	gm 1.67	14.35	5.25	3.94	per cent 6.57	per cent 28.95	per cent 22.5 23.0	per cent 26.8	moles. 1.1:1	per cent of standard 25–50
2nd	0.400	27.3	8.99	3.05	..	..	..	..	..	50
3rd	0.210	31.6	9.83	..	..	..	..	..	..	..
4th	0.100	30.9	9 93	..	..	..	..	..	..	..
5th	0.050	..	11.33	..	..	..	..	..	..	..
Insoluble brucine salt	1.464	34.0	12.03	..	5.88	25.90	21.3 22.8	23.9	2.8:1	120–130
	..	..	..	..	:	..		..	..	..

3

Table III demonstrates how the sulphur content increases from 1 atom to approximately 3 atoms per molecule of uronic acid, the anticoagulant activity simultaneously rising from 25—50 to 125 per cent of the activity of the standard heparin used for the preparation of the brucine salts.

Assuming that the disaccharide unit has an internal structure similar to that of ordinary disaccharides, there would be four hydroxyl groups available which could be esterified with sulphuric acid. Consequently the mono-, di-, tri- and tetra-sulphuric acids of mucoitin would come into question. The sodium salts of these would have the following composition.

			Molecular weight	Sulphur
Monosulphuric acid	$C_{14} H_{19} S O_{14} N Na_2$;	503.25;	6.36 %
Disulphuric	»	$C_{14} H_{18} S_2 O_{17} N Na_3$;	605.25;	10.58 %
Trisulphuric	»	$C_{14} H_{17} S_3 O_{20} N Na_4$;	707.25;	13.58 %
Tetrasulphuric	»	$C_{14} H_{16} S_4 O_{23} N Na_5$;	809.25;	15.81 %

The barium salt of the disulphuric acid contains 8.62 per cent of sulphur and that of the trisulphuric acid 10.8 per cent.

If ox liver heparin is fractionated as brucine salt, the different fractions show an increased activity with increasing sulphur content. (Table IV.)

TABLE IV

The Calcium Salts Recovered on Removal of Brucine from the Different Fractions of Brucine Salts

Substance recovered from	Air-dry substance gm	Per cent of dry substance			$[\alpha]_D^{20}$ calcul. per dry substance	Heparin activity of air-dry substance. Per cent of standard
		Ash	S	Ca		
Mother liquor						
1st	7.20	29.8	8.80	10.4	+45.7°	65
2nd	0.75	29.6	10.80	10.3	+45.4°	100
3rd	1.60	30.3	11.20	..	+57.2°	100
4th	0.60	36.3	12.00	12.0	+61.8°	125
Insoluble brucine salt	2.00	33.9	12.56	12.3	+63.5°?	135—140

The influence of the sulphur content on the anticoagulant activity is most clearly demonstrated in Table V, in which are collected a series of sodium and calcium salts obtained from the most insoluble brucine salts in different preparations. As is seen from the table, the strongest samples have a sulphur content corresponding to the calculated figure for a trisulphuric acid of mucoitin.

TABLE V

Composition and Anticoagulant Activity of Heparin Fractions with a High Sulphur Content. (Jorpes 1942.)

No.	Per cent of dry substance			Anticoagulant activity of the dry substance in per cent of standard (dry substance)
	S	Ca	Na	
1. Na salt	11.73			125
2. » »	12.00			125—130
3. » »	12.10			125—130
4. » »	12.5			135—145
5. Ca »	12.56	12.60		135—140
6. Na »	12.90			140—145
7. Ca »	13.2	12.60		153
8. Na »	13.6		10.43	160

The heparin preparations obtained from ox liver are thus not homogeneous. The different fractions obtained by means of brucine or by precipitating the strongest fractions as barium salts seem to contain the same polysaccharide, although esterified with sulphuric acid to different degrees. They each have an anticoagulant activity which decreases with the decreasing sulphur content.

The question arises as to whether or not these fractions are artefacts obtained through the influence of the reagents used in the preparation of the heparin. It is quite evident that the original polysaccharide may be destroyed under unfavourable conditions. Analytical evidence, however, does not support the assumption that such a destruction takes place during preparation. The strongest and most highly esterified

heparin polysaccharide is, in fact, very resistant to hydrolytic agents and is recovered unchanged if submitted to the
same treatment as the crude material used for the preparation of heparin. (Jorpes 1942 a, 1943.)

»Crystalline heparin.»

Crystalline heparin has been the subject of much discussion. Fischer and Schmitz (1933) thought that they had
obtained a crystalline brucine salt of heparin, a claim which,
however, was by no means justified (see p. 27). In the same
year, Charles and Scott (1933) reported finding a semi-
crystalline preparation. Finally, in 1936 Charles and Scott
isolated a barium salt of lung heparin, which they considered to be crystalline and which has been referred to in
the literature as the pure crystalline anticoagulant. Their
preparation contained, however, only 11.5 per cent of sulphur in the free acid or 20 per cent less than in the free
acid of the liver heparin isolated from the insoluble brucine
salt by the present author in 1935. This "crystalline" barium
salt of liver and lung heparin was then studied in 1940 by
Charles and Todd, who claimed it to be a homogeneous
compound, probably identical with the preparation described by Reinert and Winterstein (1939). Both groups of
workers were still of the opinion that the compound which
they assumed to be crystalline contained 2.5 sulphur atoms
to each mucoitin unit.

The compound of Charles and Todd had a crystalline
appearance. There was, however, no convincing evidence
to justify the assumption of a crystalline structure. The
crystals were "too small and heavily twinned for X-ray
diagram". The analytical data presented did not allow any
conclusions to be drawn. The preparations were dried at
room temperature and no information was given as to their
water content. Charles and Todd, in discussing their results,
assumed that pure heparin contains 2.5 sulphate groups to
each mucoitin unit on the ground that the relation of $S:N$
was $2.5:1$. These acid polysaccharides, however, are never
completely free of traces of proteins and ammonium ions.
The N-content, therefore, does not correspond to the con-

tent of hexosamine. In fact Jaques, Waters and Charles stated in 1942 that the "crystalline" Ba-salts contained NH_4-nitrogen.

The product which Reinert and Winterstein in 1939 described as derived from "pure crystalline barium heparin" was an ordinary mixture of the different polysulphuric esters mentioned above. The sodium salt, recovered from the barium salt, contained 11.1 per cent of sulphur in the air-dry substance (11.9 per cent of the dry substance), and showed an optical activity of $+42°$, a figure which is very much lower than the rotation of the sodium salt of the strongest heparin preparations from beef liver reported here ($+63.5°$).

The barium salts, because of their low solubility in water, are well fitted for purification by repeated solution in hot water and reprecipitation on cooling, or through precipitation on cooling a solution of the barium salt, containing 20 per cent of acetic acid previously heated to 65°. The "crystals" obtained are, however, not free from sodium and ammonium ions, and their barium content varies with the acidity prevailing in the solution from which they are precipitated. Consequently they are not homogeneous.

The only possible way of obtaining a heparin salt containing only one kind of positive ions is through the free acid prepared by means of cautious electrodialysis. Otherwise mixed salts are to be expected.

As a matter of fact, the chemical nature of heparin makes it most unlikely that this polysaccharide, with its many sulphuric acid groups, could be obtained in a pure state. Still less is the probability of getting a sharply defined heparin salt. Heparin behaves like chondroitin sulphuric acid and other polysaccharides, which do not crystallize, in the ordinary sense of the word, even if the sugar units are arranged in long regular chains.

As regards the homogeneity of heparin only those preparations which have the highest sulphur content, about 13.8 per cent in the sodium salt, could possibly be homogeneous. In fact, the barium salts of the heparin prepared by Jaques (1940) from ox, dog and pig liver, and described by Jaques, Waters and Charles (1942), had about the same sulphur content, optical rotation and biological activity as

*the strongest liver heparin fraction isolated as brucine salt.
The sodium salt of this fraction contains 13.6—13.8 per
cent sulphur, has an optical activity of about +65° and
an anticoagulant activity of 160 per cent of the Swedish
standard heparin or 130 Toronto units per mg. dry substance.*

So far there is no convincing evidence which points
towards the barium salt as a homogeneous compound,
though several authors have considered it to be crystalline.
On the contrary Kuizenga and Spaulding, who in 1943
gave a detailed description of a method for the large scale
preparation of heparin from lungs, giving a very high
yield, 850,000 Toronto units per 45 kg. of lungs, succeeded
in separating two distinctly different sodium salts from
the purest barium salt assumed to be crystalline.

In any case all discussion of crystalline heparin is
meaningless in as far as the biological activity is concerned. Heparin preparations obtained from one and the
same organ, e. g. beef liver, show a variation in strength
between 60 and 160 per cent varying with the sulphur
content (9 to 13.6 per cent).

This discrepancy is still more marked if the heparin preparations from different animals are compared. The most
unexpected results were obtained by Jaques, and by Jaques
and Waters in 1940 when comparing presumably crystalline
barium salts of lung heparin from different animals. In
spite of the high sulphur content in all of them, 10.8, 10.8,
10.4, and 11.6 per cent in heparin from dogs, cows, pigs
and sheep respectively, they showed a quite different anticoagulant activity, dog heparin being 2.4 times stronger
than heparin from the cow, the pig heparin 44 per cent
weaker than that from the cow and sheep heparin still
weaker. These findings of Jaques have been fully confirmed by the present author (Jorpes 1942). A statement
to the opposite effect made by Wolfrom et. al. 1945 cannot
influence the discussion. These authors were not able to
find any difference in the strength of the heparins from
different mammalian species. The contrary view held by
the above-mentioned authors seems to be well founded.

Thus it is evident that factors other than the esterification of the polysaccharide with sulphuric acid decidedly influence the anticoagulant activity.

The barium salt recrystallized from acetic acid five times by Wolfrom and co-workers (1943) also underwent, through the influence of the warm acetic acid solution, a considerable transformation without loss of sulphate groups but with complete loss of biological activity, probably due to depolymerization, and with the appearance of free NH_2-groups.

It has so far been impossible to obtain a heparin preparation which could be considered as pure heparin with well defined chemical and physiological properties. The possibility of obtaining such a substance seems on the contrary to be very remote.

A provisional international standard heparin.

In November 1942 a provisional international heparin standard was defined by the Department of Biological Standards of the National Institute for Medical Research, London. Owing to the inability of the Permanent Commission on Biological Standardization of the Health Organization of the League of Nations to perform its duties during the war the National Institute for Medical Research, London, took the initiative in defining a provisional heparin standard to be supplied through that body (Bulletin of the Health Organization of the League of Nations, Vol. X No. 2 Extract No. 1 b, M. 49). *A water free sodium salt of heparin*, obtained from a "crystalline" barium salt, supplied by the Connaught Laboratories of the University of Toronto, was selected as standard. It contained 130 Toronto units per mg., thus approximating the strength of the strongest sodium salts of heparin from ox liver or 160 per cent of the strength of the Swedish standard heparin.

Chemically this preparation is not well defined with 12.45 per cent of sulphur and 5.16 per cent of nitrogen as compared with the 13.6—13.8 per cent of sulphur and about 1.6 per cent of nitrogen occurring in the strongest sodium salts of ox liver heparin. The high nitrogen content also indicates a contamination with impurities containing nitrogen or with ammonium salts. These details do not, however, lessen the value of the preparation as a standard heparin.

At the same time the provisional international heparin unit was defined as the activity of 1/130 mg. of the standard heparin.

The Properties of Heparin.

The findings of Howell as to the properties of heparin have been fully substantiated in the more recent work. The solubility and precipitability have already been described in connection with the methods of preparation. Very little has been added to the methods of precipitating the heparin salts as used by Howell, i. e. with barium chloride, barium hydroxide, basic lead acetate, or glacial acetic acid. The writer found that it gives a precipitate with quinine and elaborated a technique for its fractionation with brucine. The morphine and cinchonine salts were easily soluble in water. Charles and Scott, who in 1936 verified the high content of ester sulphates in heparin, used an insoluble benzidine salt for its purification. Furthermore, Chargaff and Olson in 1938 found that heparin gives an insoluble precipitate with protamine.

The free acid, as obtained by electrodialysis, is easily soluble in methyl and ethyl alcohol, acetone, and glacial acetic acid. It will not dialyse through a parchment membrane and in any case only inconsiderably through a collodion membrane. The alkali and ammonium salts are precipitated with several volumes of alcohol and acetone but only in the presence of foreign electrolytes such as sodium or magnesium chloride. The calcium salt is not precipitated by one volume of methyl alcohol; it gives an opalescence with one volume of ethyl alcohol, and flocculates on the addition of 1.5 volumes of acetone. The barium salts are readily precipitated by one volume of these solvents. In neutral solution heparin is almost completely precipitated by one volume of acetone in the presence of salts. The heparin is resistant to all kinds of chemical agents.

The resistance to acid hydrolysis.

When the increase in reducing-power during hydrolysis with acids was determined, the observation was made that the fractions with the higher content of sulphur display a greater resistance to the acid. The samples with the highest sulphur content showed a very small breakdown when boiled in 15 per cent (by weight) sulphuric acid (Jorpes and Bergström 1937). Table VI indicates that it is the esterification that at least partly stabilizes the polysaccharide. This property explains the difficulties of the earlier workers. Thus the naphthoresorcinol reaction turned negative (Charles and Scott 1933 and 1936, Jorpes 1935)

TABLE VI

Rate of Hydrolysis of Heparin Samples Compared with Their Degree of Esterification

	Lung heparin	Liver heparin				Chondroitin sulphuric acid	Synthetic chondroitin polysulphuric acid
S calculated on basis of dry substance							
	per cent	per cent	per cent	per cent	per cent	per cent	per cent
	10.95	10.70	6.53	4.49	1.44	..	10.9
Hydrolysis at 100° C. in 7.5 per cent (by volume) H_2SO_4							
min.							
5	1.89	1.26	3.76	4.65	7.55	13.0	7.4
10	2.83	2.52	5.30	7.76	12.6	20.5	15.4
20	5.11	2.99	11.7	14.2	17.7	31.4	24.5
40	8.65	7.08	18.9	23.3	25.3	35.0	27 8
60	11.80	10.22	23.2	28.7	30.5	35.6	29.8

The figures give the reducing-power (Shaffer-Somogyi method) expressed as glucose in per cent of organic material.

because the hexuronic acid is not liberated on short boiling and will be destroyed during a more drastic treatment with hydrochloric acid.

The behaviour of heparin on boiling with 4 N hydrochloric acid has been studied by Wolfrom and Karabinos (1945). Only d-glucosamine was obtained, the uronic acid being successively destroyed when liberated.

It would also appear as if this esterification gives heparin its resistance to all kinds of chemical agents.

It should be pointed out, however, that heating, even with weak acids, gives rise to a depolymerization of the polysaccharide, whereby the biological activity is lost, although the increase in the reducing power is not so marked (Wolfrom and co-workers 1945).

The physico-chemical properties.

The electrical conductance, the cataphoretic mobility, and the osmotic pressure of different heparin preparations have been investigated by Wilander (1938 a).

The high content of ester sulphates gives heparin a strong electric charge. In 2 per cent solution the free acid is completely dissociated, giving a specific conductance of 85×10^{-4}. These figures refer to the strongest preparations with high sulphur content. The rate of cataphoretic mobility is $17—19 \times 10^{-5}$ cm.^{2} v.$^{-1}$ sec.$^{-1}$ and remains constant within the entire pH range of 2 to 8. The corresponding figure for chondroitin sulphuric acid is 16×10^{-5}.

The osmotic properties of heparin show a very interesting feature. In spite of the marked dissociation it exerts an extremely low osmotic pressure in aqueous solution. In a solution with 25 mg. of calcium salt, containing 10.97 per cent Ca per cubic centimetre, the depression of the freezing-point was only 0.038° C., corresponding to a molar concentration of 0.02. The molarity of the amount of calcium in the solution was 0.068, which alone with complete ionization should give seven times as great a depression of the freezing-point. This is the same phenomenon which E. Hammarsten (1924) studied in another strongly acidic compound of high-mole-

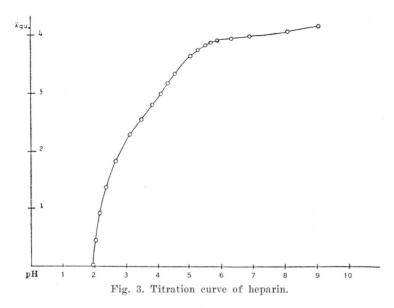

Fig. 3. Titration curve of heparin.

cular weight, the thymonucleic acid of cell nuclei. Both these substances in aqueous solution show only a fraction of the osmotic pressure which the degree of ionization would lead one to expect. The phenomenon involves an interesting protective mechanism in which nature has taken refuge to avoid high osmotic pressure and the resulting displacement of fluid when compounds of high electric charge are deposited in cells.

The phenomenon in question, the mechanism of which is not easily explained, reminds one of how animals and plants store carbohydrate in the form of osmotically inactive, high molecular polysaccharides. In the present case the mechanism is still more complicated.

The low osmotic pressure is an important detail in connection with the use of heparin. In contrast to the effect of the oxalate, heparin has no osmotic influence on the red blood cells.

The titration curve of heparin (Fig. 3, Wilander) clearly shows the existence of the carboxyl group. The free acid,

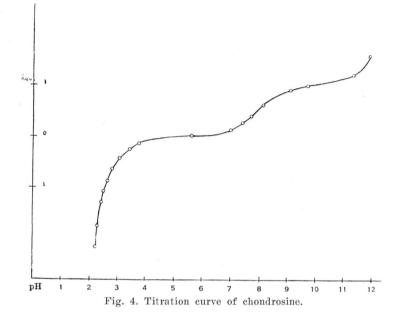

Fig. 4. Titration curve of chondrosine.

as obtained through electrodialysis of one of the strongest preparations, consumed in reaching pH 6.30 an amount of alkali, 0.0826 m. equiv. NaOH, corresponding to one carboxyl group on three sulphate groups, 0.063 m. equiv.— $O—SO_2OH$. The titration curve of chondroitin sulphuric acid behaved similarly, showing complete neutralization at pH 5. The titration curve of cellulose trisulphuric acid, where the carboxyl group is lacking, however, showed a different course, already reaching a maximum at pH 3, when the sulphate groups were neutralized.

Furthermore, the titration curves showed that the amino group in heparin is not free. In Wilander's experiments there was only a trace of buffering capacity between pH 7 and 9, whereas the chondrosine, where the amino group is free, showed a distinct rise of the curve in this region (Fig. 4).

CHAPTER II

The Mode of Action of Heparin.

Howell advanced the view that heparin interferes in the first phase of coagulation, preventing the formation of thrombin from prothrombin. He had found that it did not prevent the action of thrombin on fibrinogen solutions. Mellanby, however, in 1934, working with an artificial coagulation system consisting of purified prothrombin or thrombin and fibrinogen solutions and a highly diluted watery extract of testis as kinase, came to quite different conclusions. In the first place, heparin did not prevent the activation of the purified prothrombin in the presence of kinase and calcium ions. Secondly, it acted as a thrombin inhibitor in the presence of the normal salts of the plasma. The anti-thrombin activity was not observed in a dialyzed salt-free plasma. Furthermore, the inactivated thrombin could be completely re-activated by adding kinase, the quantity of kinase necessary for re-activation being in a direct numerical relation to the amount of heparin present.

The action of heparin on thrombin was explained by Quick in 1938 as the result of the combined influence of heparin and a fraction of the serum albumins, the normal serum antithrombin. Without heparin the affinity of fibrinogen for thrombin is stronger than that of the plasma albumin, but in the presence of heparin the albumin-heparin compound competes with the fibrinogen for thrombin, thus becoming a strong thrombin inhibitor. In this reaction neutral salts are necessary.

The importance of this plasma factor was stressed by Brinkhous, Smith, Warner and Seegers in 1939. They found that heparin alone had an inhibitory effect on thrombin, as had been claimed by Mellanby, but that heparin and plasma albumins together were a very strong prothrombin inhibitor. The plasma factor is separated from the prothrombin when the latter is precipitated with ammonium sulphate. Crystalline serum albumin together with heparin has no inhibiting effect on thrombin (Ferguson 1940). In 1942 Seegers, Warner, Brinkhous and Smith showed that heparin in minute quantities, 1 mg. to 1 litre of plasma, accelerates the antithrombic activity of the plasma, thus functioning as a catalyst in the destruction of thrombin by plasma "antithrombin". (See also Seegers and Smith 1943.) The antithrombic property of plasma has been studied by Volkert. (See Astrup 1944.) It is concentrated in a certain albumin fraction precipitable at 2.8 M ammonium sulphate (Stewart and Rourke 1940) and is probably enzymatic in nature.

Jaques and Mustard in 1940 repeated the experiments of the previous authors. They found that the serum proteins were essential for the action of heparin as claimed by Howell and Holt, Quick, and Brinkhous and co-workers, and they confirmed Howell's findings that heparin is inactive in preventing the thrombin effect on pure fibrinogen. If added to thoroughly dialyzed serum the heparin had, contrary to the statement of Mellanby, a full effect, but an addition of sodium chloride up to 0.4 per cent tends to neutralize the action of heparin. Above this concentration of the sodium chloride the heparin activity is enhanced. The curves expressing the anticoagulant activity of heparin obtained after addition of sodium chloride did not show any resemblance to those obtained either with the original plasma or the dialyzed plasma.

A very prominent feature in the reaction mechanism of heparin is the mutual neutralizing effect of heparin and thrombokinase. Experiments pertaining to the stoechiometric course of this reaction were carried out by Wadsworth and Maltaner in 1937. The interference of the heparin in the first phase of coagulation and the neutralizing effect of cephalin on heparin was also demonstrated by Ferguson in 1937 and 1938. He found the action of heparin on prothrombin to be ten times stronger than on the activated thrombin. It is not clear whether this reaction is direct or indirect. Further discussion is hampered by the scantiness of our knowledge of the thromboplastin, which is assumed to be a lipoprotein, possibly acting as a proteolytic enzyme (Eagle 1937) splitting off from the prothrombin some kind of prothrombin inhibitor.

From this it is evident that the heparin has a multiple effect acting on both the thrombin and on the prothrombin and also on the thromboplastin either directly or through the prothrombin.

It is not known, however, in what way heparin interferes with the processes leading to the formation of thrombin and fibrin. At first, it seemed plausible to assume a physico-chemical interaction between the heparin and some of the components of the coagulation system (Jorpes 1938).

The Significance of the Electric Charge in the Heparin Effect.

Our knowledge of the chemistry of heparin seems to allow us to draw certain conclusions as to its mode of action. Its properties clearly indicate that its interference in the coagulation process can hardly be anything but a physico-chemical reaction. Since the amino group is acetylated, heparin has no reactive groups in its molecule. On the other hand, its physico-chemical properties are quite unique. It has a high molecular weight and carries an exceptionally strong electric charge, apparently the strongest of all the organic compounds of the animal body (Fig. 5). The strongest preparations, which contain 13.6 per cent of sulphur in the sodium salt, corresponding to 15.5 per cent in the free acid, consist of up to no less than 45 per cent of sulphuric acid, really a peculiar product of synthesis in the living organism. The strongest compounds of a similar nature hitherto known, the nucleic acids, contain only 25 per cent of phosphoric acid. It is therefore not unreasonable to presume that heparin in some way or other changes the charge of the prothrombin or the kinase, thus prevent-

Fig. 5. Scheme demonstrating the accumulation of electric charges on
the heparin polysaccharide. Two disaccharide units contain six
-O-SO₂OH groups (━) and two -COOH groups (—).

ing the formation of thrombin, or does the same with the
thrombin.

It was also evident that the anticoagulant activity increased with increasing sulphur content. Furthermore the
increase in sulphur causes a greater increase in the activity,
if introduced in the highly esterified samples, thus indicating that it is the abundance of ionic charges that makes the
polysaccharide an anticoagulant.

The assumption of the importance of the acidic groups
was beautifully supported by the introduction of sulphuric
acid groups into ordinary polysaccharides, all of which gave
an anticoagulant effect.

Attempted synthesis of anticoagulants.

To test the assumption of the importance of the acidic
groups, various polysaccharide sulphuric acids were synthesized (Bergström 1935, 1936). The polysaccharides, cellulose,
chitin, pectic acid, glycogen, starch, and gum arabic, as
well as yeast nucleic acid and chondroitin sulphuric acid,
were treated with chlorosulphonic acid, $ClSO_2OH$, in pyridine. After the treatment the preparations contained 17—
19 per cent of sulphur, corresponding to three groups of
sulphuric acid to each glucose molecule. The compounds
were tested in neutral aqueous solution and were found to
have an anticoagulant effect, as will be seen from Table VII.

TABLE VII

Anticoagulant Activity of some Synthetic Polysaccharide Poly-sulphuric Acids. The Activity of the Heparin Hynson, Dunning and Westcott (No. 126) is expressed as Unity (Bergström 1936).

The strongest natural heparin obtained . . . 13
Synthetic chondroitin polysulphuric acid . . 1 $1/2$—2
Chitin disulphuric acid . . . . 1 $1/2$
Cellulose trisulphuric acid 1
Polysulphuric ester of pectic acid 1
Starch trisulphuric acid . . . . $1/2$
Glycogen trisulphuric acid . . . . $1/12$—$1/3$
Sulphuric esters of gum arabic . . . . . . $1/4$
Sulphuric esters of yeast nucleic acid . . . . $1/12$

Sulphuric acid esters of monosaccharides and disaccharides have no anticoagulant influence. The polysaccharides with a comparatively high molecular weight, such as cellulose, chitin, and the pectins, which are rather resistant to acid hydrolysis, gave the strongest anticoagulant effect upon being esterified. According to Haworth, Hirst, and others, cellulose has at least 200 glucose units in the molecule, where-as starch has but 24—30 units. The latter, too, is much more easily depolymerized by the influence of acid during the esterification. Starch and glycogen also gave considerably weaker preparations. This may partly depend on the break-ing-down of the molecule. In Bergström's experiments, for instance, if chondroitin sulphuric acid was treated too long with the chlorosulphonic acid, the activity of the prepar-ations rapidly fell owing to depolymerization. Even if the anticoagulant effect of these preparations is considerably weaker than that of the strongest natural heparin, the re-action mechanism would appear to be similar in both cases. A galactan sulphuric acid occurring in the red alga *Chondrus crispus*, was also found by Bergström to have a certain, though weak, anticoagulant activity.

Similar synthetic experiments were carried out simul-taneously with the same results by Chargaff, Bancroft, and Stanley-Brown (1936), who also mention the activity of galactan sulphuric acid in the alga *Irideae laminarioides*. The activity of the corresponding substance in *Chondrus crispus* and other algae has been studied by Elsner, Broser, and Bürgel (1937), and by Elsner (1938).

A polysaccharide with a very high content of ester sulphate and an anticoagulant activity reported to be far stronger than that of Heparin Kahlbaum was isolated from the mucus of *Charonia lampas* by Soda and Egami in 1938. It contained 15 per cent of sulphur, thus about four sulphate groups for each disaccharide unit. The organic skeleton consisted of equal parts of a uronic acid and another sugar.

Chargaff and co-workers arrived at the conclusion that in order to be able to act as an anticoagulant, a substance should be of high molecular weight and contain groups of ester sulphuric acid or other acidic groups of corresponding strength. They mentioned, however, the great difference in strength between the synthetic preparations and natural heparin.

As an expression of the importance of the acidic groups Astrup, Galsmar and Volkert (1944) note that the chitin monosulphuric acid is a fairly weak anticoagulant, whereas the chitin disulphuric acid is almost as strong as heparin, at least *in vivo*.

The question of the importance of the acidic groups has been touched upon in the earlier literature, without being appreciated to its full extent.

When first mentioned by Demole and Reinert in 1930, the acidic groups received no attention. As the natural anticoagulants, heparin and hirudin as well as novirudin, are all substances of high molecular weight, these authors endeavoured to find new anticoagulants among synthetic products with large molecules. No polypeptides were found to be active. In the aromatic group, however, both acidic and basic compounds had a certain anticoagulant effect. The lignine sulphonic acids were the strongest of all the synthetic products. They found the most suitable product to be the sodium salt of polyanethol sulphonic acid, which later came on the market as Liquoid Roche. Thus in this case a strongly acidic compound with a high molecular weight was found to possess anticoagulant activity.

The same year, 1930, Stuber and Land pointed out the anticoagulant effect of Germanin (Bayer 205).

Albert Fischer, who in 1931 studied the influence of Germanin on proteins, expressed the view that heparin produces its effect by displacing the isoelectric point of the prothrombin and other blood proteins. He considered that the heparin brought about this effect through its carboxyl groups. He observed how heparin *in vitro* displaced the flocculation optimum of casein to a lower pH value, and he made use of this detail for the quantitative determination of heparin (1932). To him the heparin effect was a purely physico-chemical phenomenon caused by a colloid with a strong electro-negative charge, a point of view which we would now have still better reason to accept.

The characteristic structure of heparin and the synthesis of the polysaccharide sulphuric acids, attracted interest to the dominating importance of the electric charge as an active factor in the anticoagulants, and Heinz Herrmann at Fischer's laboratory in 1937 pursued this line of reasoning. He assumed that basic substances also ought to be active. This assumption proved to be correct. Here, too, compounds of low molecular weight such as basic amino acids and biogenic amines were inactive. On the other hand, basic dyes were found to be active, some displaying the same activity as Heparin Kahlbaum. Methylene blue, methyl green, and crystal violet were active. They had about one-third of the activity of the preparation just mentioned. Janus green and Janus black were of the same strength as the commercial heparin previously available, these substances being strongly ionized quaternary ammonia bases.

In addition to these fairly convincing proofs of a physico-chemical mechanism, other details point in the same direction. The heparin effect can thus be inhibited simply by diluting the heparin blood or the plasma with distilled water, or by introducing carbon dioxide, e. g. in weakly heparinized blood and peptone plasma of the dog. Heparin can *in vitro* be completely removed from the blood by adding a solution of toluidine blue (Holmgren and Wilander 1937). This substance reacts with heparin and precipitates it even in a very dilute solution. Heparinized blood, to which a solution of toluidine blue has been added, clots in a few minutes. In the same way it can be made to clot by adding protamine, which through its basic ionic charge neutralizes heparin (Chargaff and Olson 1938). This indicates that heparin is loosely bound to the components upon which it acts.

A quite different view as to the action mechanism of heparin is expressed by Wolfrom and McNeely (1945). They found that the content of amino-nitrogen increases proportionally to the decrease in anticoagulant activity on boiling an acid heparin solution, and they therefore supposed that the seat of biological activity in the heparin molecule is its nitrogen linkage.

Thus the chemical nature of heparin, the synthesis experiments and the possibility of inactivating heparin *in vivo* by means of such mild agents as the protamine, which only neutralizes the negative electric charges of the heparin, seem to indicate that the anticoagulant effect is due to the electric charge of the molecule. The strong influence of the neutral salts of the plasma as pointed out by Mellanby, Quick and by Jaques and Mustard, is to be interpreted in the same way.

The action of heparin is in many respects similar to that of the synthetic detergents. As shown by Putnam and Neurath in 1945, anionic detergents like sodium dodecyl sulphate act upon proteins even on the alkaline side of the iso-electric range, where the anionic detergent reacts with the basic charges with opposite sign in the anionic protein complex. This discussion applies directly to the heparin polysaccharide carrying a negative charge in a medium containing anionic proteins. It is therefore not surprising that heparin has an exceedingly strong action upon the haemolytic complement and on different enzymes. Evidently, the reaction mechanism is the same here as on the proteins of the coagulation system.

A large molecule is essential, as proved also to be the case in the synthesis experiments. The anticoagulant activity is easily destroyed on heating a slightly acid heparin solution, even if the reducing power is only slightly increased. Thus "recrystallization" of the barium salt in acetic acid at 60° C is followed by loss of activity (Wolfrom et. al. 1943) evidently due to depolymerization. The degree of polymerization is certainly of no less importance than the esterification with sulphuric acid, particularly as there is no close relationship between the sulphur content and the anticoagulant activity of heparin preparations from different animals.

The reactivation of thrombin, inhibited by heparin on the addition of an appropriate amount of kinase also indicates that there is a very loose linkage between the heparin and the thrombin.

The Effect of Heparin on Systems Other than Those Involved in Coagulation.

Thanks to its extraordinary physical properties, heparin also reacts with blood proteins other than the coagulation enzymes. The reaction most thoroughly studied is that on *haemolytic complement*, or its 'mid-piece'. Heparin still neutralizes complement in a very dilute solution, the concentration being about the same as for its action upon prothrombin (Hedenius and Snellman 1937, Wising 1937). Hans J. Fuchs (1928, 1931, 1933), who has shown great interest in this question, considered prothrombin to be identical with the mid-piece of complement, owing to their similarity as regards precipitability and mode of reaction. To him this was not only an empirical finding, but an expression of a mutual connection between the two most important protective mechanisms of the blood, the coagulation and the bactericidal immunity reactions. Although the similarity is striking, the two components cannot be identical. As demonstrated by Quick (1935), the transformation of prothrombin into thrombin causes no decrease in the complement content. Furthermore, prothrombin is adsorbed on aluminium hydroxide, whereas complement is not (see T. N. B. Osborne, *Complement or Alexin*, London, 1937). Inhibiting substances like heparin and synthetic polysaccharide polysulphuric esters exert quite a different influence on the two components (Wising 1938, Wilander 1938, Ecker and Pillemer 1941).

In any case, heparin and also Germanin, have a strong affinity for complement. According to von Falkenhausen (1931) the reaction with heparin is reversible, similar to that with prothrombin, and can be reversed by an excess of haemolytic amboceptor, whereas Germanin and salvarsan are said to have an irreversible influence.

Among the other components of the plasma influenced by heparin the *iso-agglutinins* may be mentioned. The influence on them is much weaker than on the constituents previously discussed.

An unexplained reaction occurs when heparin is injected in animals with lipaemia after a meal. 0.5—5 minutes after injection of 2.5 mg. of heparin intravenously in a dog the lipaemia disappears, a reaction which does not take place *in vitro* (Hahn 1943).

As is to be expected, heparin exerts an inhibiting influence on different enzymes. According to Fischer and Herrmann (1937) it interferes with *the enzyme system fumarase-fumaric acid*, causing a complete inhibition in a concentration of 0.05 per cent. It also inhibits the proteolysis of various substrates by trypsin (Horwitt 1940, Glazko and Ferguson 1940).

On the other hand, heparin itself is not attacked by the digestive enzymes and is consequently not taken up by the intestine (Astrup, Galsmar and Volkert 1944).

Some cellular processes like the phagocytosis of staphylococci by polymorphonuclear leucocytes *in vivo* are apparently not affected by heparin (Rigdon and Wilson 1941), nor are the capillary permeability, the microscopic signs of inflammation, or the localization of the leucocytes in the area of inflammation. Heparinization of rabbits, likewise, does not have any influence upon the phagocytosis of the cells of the reticulo-endothelial system (Rigdon and Schrantz 1942).

As an expression of the physico-chemical reaction mechanism Øllgäard (1943) found that heparin prevents the agglutination of the thrombocytes brought about by adding mercuric cyanide, mercuric chloride or saponin to citrated plasma and digesting it at 42° C for 3 hours.

Dragstedt, Wells and Rocha e Silva (1942) found that heparin prevents the release of histamine into plasma from the erythrocytes in rabbit's blood on addition of trypsin (0.5 mg./ml.), proteose (5 mg./ml.) or an antigen. This most interesting reaction is fully inhibited if 1.2 mg. of heparin is added to one ml. of rabbit's blood prior to the addition of the releasing agent. The amount of heparin necessary is much higher than that necessary to keep the blood fluid.

Opinions differ very greatly regarding the influence of heparin on *anaphylactic shock*. Keys, Preston, and Strauser (1926) observed in 1922 that when given 45 minutes before the anaphylactic dose, heparin protects sensitized pigeons from shock, and later Williams, Rene, and van der Carr (1927, 1928) demonstrated the same for guinea pigs sensitized with horse serum. Their experiments seem to have been carried out with great care, and the anaphylactic reaction was studied in the Dale test on uterine strips and according to the Koessler-Lewis bronchospasm method. However, these results have been disputed by Hanzlik and coworkers (1927), by Reed and Lamson (1927), and by Reed (1930).

A mitigating influence on the glomerulonephritic changes following an injection of horse serum in rabbits immunized against it was observed by Silfverskiöld (1940). If the animals received 75 mg. of heparin intravenously shortly before the third and the subsequent horse serum injections, the renal reaction was milder or absent. Albumin, red cells and casts appeared in the urine of the non-heparinized rabbits.

The inhibitory effect of heparin on *cellular growth* and on *differentiation of the tissues* is a very complicated one. It has been demonstrated by several investigators, A. Fischer (1927, 1936), Goerner (1930), and has been especially studied by Zakrzewski (1932 a and b, 1933).

Hitherto heparin has been treated as a physiological

anticoagulant, which participates in keeping the blood fluid. Recently a quite different view as to its function in the body has been advanced independently by two authors, Magerl (1942) and P. Astrup (1945). *They consider that heparin plays a part in the immunization processes taking place in the body.* Since our present knowledge of these processes is very meagre, the discussion of this topic must be postponed.

CHAPTER III

The Site of Formation of Heparin.

In the early stages of the study of heparin, the liver was considered to be its source, and as an anticoagulant it was also assumed to occur in the vascular system. Attempts were made to prepare anti-prothrombin from the walls of the large blood vessels. Wöhlisch's monograph of 1929 contains a detailed account of those experiments. Owing to poor technique and the complete lack of knowledge as to the chemistry of heparin, the experiments were of very limited value. In the assay the heparin effect could be counteracted and hidden by the addition of kinase to the samples. Even though Hiruma (1923), using extraction with 1 per cent saline solution, reported that 'in der Intima und überhaupt in der Gefässwand grosse Mengen von Anti-prothrombin enthalten sind', these early experiments were not very convincing. A somewhat clearer result was obtained by Fuchs in 1930. With his method, which was also used by Howell, samples from the walls of the larger vessels showed a fairly good heparin activity. The only detail missing in the experiments of Fuchs was the chemical identification of the anticoagulating factor.

In 1933, Charles and Scott with their improved method of preparation could isolate highly active heparin from the liver, as well as from the lungs, spleen, kidneys, etc. The lungs were especially rich in heparin, which was thus demonstrated to be a constituent of ordinary tissues.

The present author, in 1936, endeavoured to repeat Fuchs's experiments in order to prepare heparin from the walls of large vessels. The method used for the liver and lungs was applied to blood vessels of cattle, and heparin of the same chemical nature was found there also. The aorta of cattle gave a good yield of a preparation one-eighth as strong as liver heparin and with a correspondingly low sulphur content (5.2 per cent). This first experiment acted as a stimulus to further investigations.

Nevertheless, in two later samples from the aorta of pigs no heparin at all was obtained, and consequently the original result appeared rather doubtful. After these two failures the question would have been left at the same stage as after the studies of the earlier investigators, had not certain observations been made in regard to toluidine blue which stains heparin strongly metachromatically (Jorpes, 1936). These stimulated the author to try another line of approach. Attempts were made to demonstrate the presence of heparin directly in the walls of the large vessels by immersing them in a dilute solution 0.01 pro mille of toluidine blue. Within a few hours this resulted in a very beautiful purple staining of the vessel walls which in cross-section was most marked as it approached the lumen. Simultaneously it was found that the content of ester sulphates in the inner fifth of the aortic wall was twice that in the outer four-fifths. All this could be considered to indicate the presence of heparin in the inner part of the vascular wall, a supposition which appeared very plausible. Similar findings were made in regard to the eye, the inside of the cornea, the capsule of the lens, the iris, and the vitreous body, all of which were stained metachromatically with toluidine blue. There was good reason to expect heparin here in view of the fact, well known to ophthalmologists, that minor haemorrhages in the eye generally do not coagulate. However, these findings could not be given a uniform interpretation, as, according to Lison (1935 a and b, 1936), the toluidine blue reaction is specific only for high molecular esters of sulphuric acid. His investigation referred primarily to chondroitin sulphuric acid. This very compound occurs in the wall of the aorta (Levene, 1925) as does mucoitin sulphuric acid in the cornea and in the vitreous body (Levene, 1925, Meyer, and Palmer, 1936 a and b). Thus it was still impossible to obtain decisive information as to the heparin content of the blood vessels.

Pursuing the idea still further, and staining the tissues histologically with toluidine blue, we arrived at an unexpected and very interesting solution of the problem.

Heparin and the Ehrlich Mast Cells or Heparinocytes.

A purely chemical observation had furthermore accentuated the desirability of demonstrating the location of heparin in the tissues. In the beginning it appeared reasonable to presume heparin to be a more highly esterified chondroitin sulphuric acid, whereby its occurrence in the lungs, in the annular cartilages of the bronchi, could be expected. When the amino sugar had proved to be glucosamine (Jorpes and Bergström 1936) and not galactosamine as in chondroitin sulphuric acid, it was evident that heparin had no direct connection with the chondroitin sulphuric acid and the cartilage. It was then reasonable to think of the great number of blood vessels in the lungs and the liver as the source of heparin, and this supposition also fitted in with the prevailing conception of its physiological function.

The old idea of heparin being localized to the vascular system appeared in a new form. We then sought the co-operation of a histologist, Hjalmar Holmgren, in order to apply toluidine blue staining histologically. The histologist could very soon inform us that the colour anticipated was really obtained in the lungs as well as in the liver in a type of cell long referred to as the mast cell of Ehrlich. Such cells are found mainly in the connective tissue in the vicinity of the capillaries and in the walls of the blood vessels. Histologically these cells have been stained with basic dyes, thionin and toluidine blue, which give a metachromatic purple instead of blue colour to the granules as well as to the cartilage and mucus. In this case the histological picture was quite typical. The granules of the mast cells were stained dark purple, whereas the rest of the section had taken up very little or nothing of the basic dye. The nucleic acids in the nuclei of the cells were not always

stained. An investigation was then carried out by Holmgren and Wilander (1937), and the granules of the mast
cells of Ehrlich were proved to consist of heparin. The
essential points in the argument are as follows.

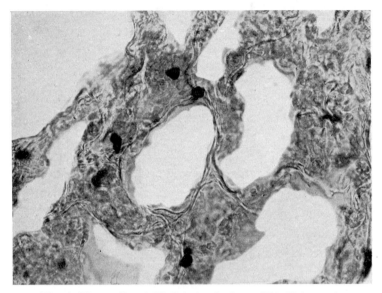

Fig. 6. Mast cells of Ehrlich in the lung (Hj. Holmgren).

As demonstrated by Lison, the purple colour obtained with
toluidine blue is specific for sulphuric esters of high molecular
weights. Phenol sulphuric acid and other low molecular esters
give either no colour or a weak one. The phosphoric esters
are not stained. The cerebroside sulphuric acid studied by
G. Blix (1937) gives only a weak purple stain. Being a
polysulphuric ester with a high molecular weight, heparin
gives a very strong colour, a hundred times stronger than
that obtained with the same quantity of chondroitin sulphuric acid, and furthermore, the tint is a pure purple.
Holmgren and Wilander discovered that heparin is precipitated by toluidine blue from very dilute solutions. The
dye also removes the heparin from heparinized blood, which
regains its clotting capacity. In any case, toluidine blue

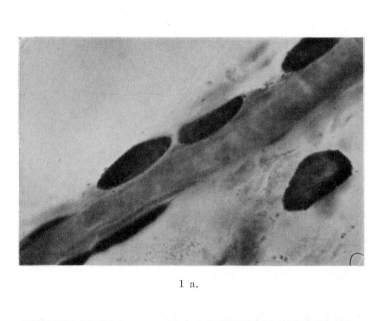

1 a.

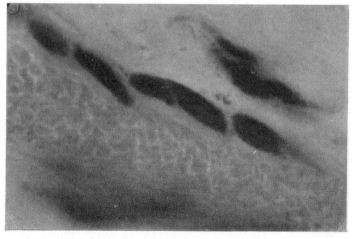

1 b.

Mast cells, heparinocytes, around capillaries in the subcutaneous
tissue of the rat. Vital staining. 1×700.

possesses an extremely strong affinity for heparin. That fact, together with the specificity of the reaction, strongly supports the assumption that heparin is localized to the granules of the mast cells.

The next method adopted was the determination of the content of ester sulphates in various parenchymatous organs. This was done by hydrolysis with strong hydrochloric acid, the liberated sulphates being precipitated with barium chloride. It was now found that the content of sulphuric esters paralleled the mast cell content of the various organs. This was true not only as regards different organs in the same animal, but also with reference to the organs of different animals.

A final confirmation of this discovery was obtained on renewed analysis of the blood vessels (Jorpes, Holmgren, Wilander 1937). As the analysis of ester sulphates was of no value because the large vessels contain quantities of chondroitin sulphuric acid (in the aorta about 2—3 per cent calculated on dry substance) new preparations of heparin were made from the larger blood vessels. The above-mentioned purple colour, obtained on the inside of the thoracic and abdominal aorta with toluidine blue after immersion in a 0.01 pro mille solution of the dye, could just as well be attributed to the chondroitin sulphuric acid.

Upon histological examination Holmgren found that the aorta of the pig is practically lacking in mast cells, thus explaining why the author's two earlier preparations from this material yielded no heparin. In the very first preparation, presumed to be made from the aorta of the pig, the collection of the material had not been supervised. When later the aorta of cattle was found to contain mast cells, and the vena cava still more of them, two preparations were made from each with a very good yield in the two preparations from the inferior vena cava (Table VIII). From the latter preparations a small quantity of pure heparin, with 9.95 per cent of sulphur and the same activity as the standard heparin, was isolated from the insoluble brucine salt.

TABLE VIII

Yield of Heparin from the Walls of the Larger Vessels

Experiment	Species	Weight of tissue	Crude heparin	Heparin activity expressed in mg. of standard heparin as found per kilo of tissue
		Kilos	Grams	
1	Unknown	2.5	1.8	90
2	Pig, aorta	0.63	0.31	Trace
3	» »	3.2	0.02	0
4	Ox »	2.5	0.52	4—5
5	» »	5.4	2.78	65
6	» Vena cava inf.	4.0	1.32	100
7	» » »	3.0	1.45	120

The final proof of this connection between heparin and the mast cells was provided by Wilander. He prepared heparin according to Charles and Scott from the liver capsule and from the liver of cattle, from the liver and from the subcutaneous tissue of rats, these being organs having a very different mast-cell content. In two preparations from the liver of cattle, the amount of raw heparin per kilo of fresh liver corresponded in activity to 56 and 75 mg. of standard heparin. In two preparations from ox liver capsule the corresponding figures were 540 and 830 mg., ten times more than in the liver itself. No heparin was obtained from rat liver, which lacks mast cells, but in the subcutaneous tissue of this animal there were 63 mg. per kilo or just as much as in ox liver. (Table IX.)

The present author has repeated and confirmed these experiments of Wilander. There is no doubt whatsoever about the nature of the granular substance of the mast cells. It is heparin.

Certain details in the histological technique are in close agreement with this finding. Holmgren and Wilander observed that the best staining is obtained after fixing the organs in a solution of basic lead acetate which precipitates the heparin. If the tissue is left for some time before fixation, or if this is done without the precipitant, the result is

TABLE IX

Yield of Heparin from Different Sources with a Different Content of Mast Cells

		Yield of crude heparin	Heparin of standard potency per kg fresh organ
Ox liver capsule	2.1 kg	4.32 gm.	540 mg.
» » »	0.7 »	1.15 »	. 830 »
» »	450gm.	0.275 »	75 »
» »	400 »	0.361 »	56 »
Rat »	90 »		0 »
Subcutaneous tissue of the rat	115 »	0.085 »	63 »

generally a diffuse metachromasia due to heparin dissolved in the neighbourhood. In alcoholic solution quinine, which also precipitates heparin, has also proved valuable for fixing the granules of the mast cells.

Sufficient proof has now been brought forward to substantiate the supposition that heparin is the granular substance of the tissue mast cells.[1] As early as in 1877 Paul Ehrlich differentiated these from Waldeyer's 'Plasmazellen' by staining them with basic safranine and methyl violet. Now his specific stains, in this case toluidine blue, have also helped us to demonstrate the natural anticoagulant at the site of its formation.

Thereby, one of the old problems of histologists, the riddle of the metachromatic granules in the mast cells of Ehrlich (see the monographs of Lehner 1924 and of Michels in Downey's *Hematology*) has been solved. Owing to the relation of these cells to the vascular system and their occurrence throughout the entire vertebrate scale where the coagulating mechanism is the same, it is indeed very reasonable to presume that heparin is of importance as a natural anticoagulant.

The histological picture alone had already induced a series

---

[1] The cautious attitude toward the question about the heparin content of the mast cells held by Mann and Bollman in 1939 and by Apitz in 1942 is not justified.

of eminent anatomists, such as Maximow and Marchand to ascribe a secretory function to the tissue mast cells. Several workers, including Lehner, Brack and Marchand, have emphasized their amoeboid mobility, while others have regarded them as fixed tissue cells. Michels regards the tissue mast cells as belonging to a group of resting wandering cells as is evident from their embryonic histogenesis. They are amoeboid notwithstanding the fact that most of them are sessile. Summarizing the result of a study on human material, U. Quensel of Uppsala pointed out in 1933 that he, like Staemmler, regards the mast cells as *'einzellige Drüsen des Bindegewebes*, die demnach wohl auch ihre eigene, noch zu erforschende Funktion besitzen müssen'. He found their topography particularly characteristic, with accumulations 'an der Wand oder in der nächsten Nähe der kleinen dünnwandigen nicht muskelhaltigen Gefässe und Kapillaren'. This perivascular position is so regular and consistent that it is an essential feature of the topography of the mast cell, and cannot be regarded as accidental. 'Dabei ist zu bemerken, dass sich die Mz nur um die kleineren, nicht muskelhaltigen Gefässe und Kapillaren herum befinden, und zwar entweder dicht an der Wand oder etwas davon entfernt. Dies ist eine so häufige Erscheinung, dass sie wohl mit der noch rätselhaften Funktion der Mz in irgend einer Weise zusammenhängt.' This feature, which he demonstrated in man, is still more obvious in the subcutaneous tissues of the rat as illustrated in Fig. 7 and 8 and in the colour plate.

Thus mast cells, because of their position around the capillaries and the small blood vessels without a muscular coat, are able to void their granular contents into the perivascular tissue juices, or almost directly into the blood stream, a state of affairs which indicates that these cells, and with them the heparin, may have a physiological function to fulfil to the advantage of the blood circulation.

The lively exchange of fluid through the walls of the capillaries will be most clearly realized through the statement of de Hevesy (1946) that in the guinea pig 73 per cent of the water in the blood is exchanged for extracellular water every minute.

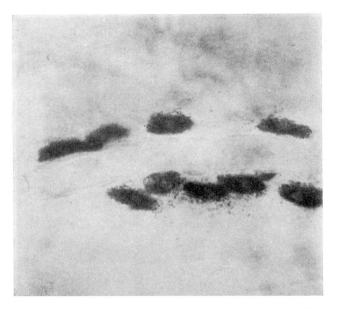

Fig. 7. Mast cells around a capillary in the subcutaneous tissue of the rat. Vital staining. 1×450.

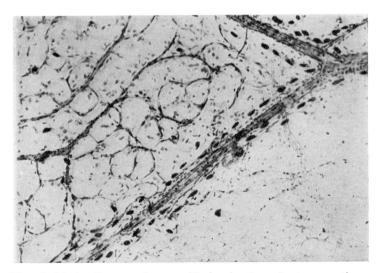

Fig. 8. Mast cells around precapillaries in the subcutaneous tissue of the rat. Vital staining.

The name heparinocytes suggested for the mast cells.

In 1943 Robert Ehrström suggested the name *heparino-cytes* for the blood leucocytes containing basophilic granules, a suggestion which is not fully justified because of the un-certain nature of these granules. The name should preferably be given to the tissue mast cells carrying heparin.

Urticaria pigmentosa due to local overproduction of heparin in the skin.

The textbooks in dermatology state that there are in urti-caria pigmentosa local accumulations of mast cells around capillaries in the skin. The appearance of multiple petechial haemorrhages all over the body in this very rare disease is therefore not surprising. The haemorrhages are particularly pronounced in newborn infants as demonstrated in a case described .by Magnusson (1947). (See colour plate.)

Peptone Shock in Dogs.

The injection of Witte's peptone into the vascular system of the dog results in very severe shock, after which the blood loses its clotting capacity (Schmidt-Mülheim 1880). This behaviour of the dog has been extensively studied by physiologists (see Wilander 1938). Preparations with an anticoagulant activity were obtained by Howell in 1924 and by Quick in 1936 from the blood of a dog in peptone shock. The general assumption has therefore been that the coagulating deficiency is caused by a secretion of heparin into the blood stream. Convincing evidence for this suppo-sition was provided in 1938 by Wilander. He isolated heparin from plasma of the peptone dog in an amount sufficient to explain the coagulation deficiency. He obtained in three different lots of dog plasma 6.4, 6, and 3.2 mg. of standard heparin per 100 ml. of blood, an amount which makes the blood completely incoagulable.

In the same year Waters, Markowitz and Jaques showed that the incoagulability of the blood both in peptone shock and in anaphylactic shock of sensitized dogs is completely inhibited by protamine. In hepatectomized animals anaphy-

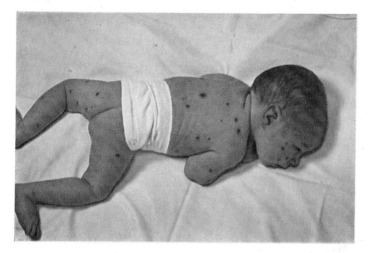

2.

Urticaria pigmentosa in an infant.

lactic shock could be produced but no incoagulability of the blood followed.

Furthermore, Jaques and Waters in 1940 isolated a barium salt of pure heparin from the blood of dogs sensitized to serum albumin and shocked by a new serum injection under amytal anaesthesia. It had the same strength as the liver heparin from dogs, being 2.5 times as strong as ox liver heparin.

Wilander was able to demonstrate histologically how during the collapse of the dog the mast cells of the liver had emptied almost all of their metachromatic granular material into the blood.

These experiments clearly show that at least in one animal, the dog, heparin can be transferred from the mast cells of the liver into the blood.

The Fate of Heparin in the Body.

We know little about the metabolism of heparin. In 1940, Jaques claimed that he had demonstrated the existence of a heparinase in rabbit liver.

A considerable part of injected heparin very soon leaves the body through the kidneys (Howell and McDonald 1930, Wilander 1938). Using metachromatic staining with toluidine blue, Wilander demonstrated that heparin, when injected intravenously into rats, accumulated in the kidneys within one minute, and after subcutaneous injection within 10 minutes. In the former case a maximum excretion was reached in 5 to 10 minutes and in the latter case in 30 minutes. A slow excretion of small amounts of heparin was still in progress after 48 hours. After intravenous injection of 50 to 300 mg. into rabbits, about 20 to 25 per cent of the injected heparin could be recovered from the urine during the first hour. During the second hour about one-tenth as much could be recovered. Biological assays were made of the crude product obtained from the urinary specimens.

These findings of Wilander were confirmed in 1941 by Copley and Schnedorf, who also used metachromatic staining to study the heparin excretion in the urine of mice and dogs.

From these experiments it is evident that a considerable part of the heparin very soon leaves the vascular system. It can also penetrate the vascular wall from outside. It is, in fact, possible to influence coagulation time by injecting heparin subcutaneously or intraperitoneally (Lehmann and Boys 1940).

CHAPTER IV

The Strength of Pure Heparin and Similar Anticoagulants.

Methods of Assay.

The methods applied in assaying heparin can be tabulated as follows (Jalling, Jorpes and Lindén 1946).

Unaltered blood.

Howell (1925)	Fresh cat blood
Scott and Charles (1933)	,,　,,　,,
Jaques and Charles (1941)	,,　,,　,,
Jorpes (1935), Wilander (1938)	Fresh ox blood
Schütz (1941)	Fresh rabbit blood

Heparinized plasma.
Neutralization of heparin with
　kinase

Dam and Glavind (1939)	Human plasma

Oxalated blood + thrombin.

Jaques and Charles (1941)	Oxalated ox blood

Citrated plasma + Ca-salt.

Reinert and Winterstein (1939)	Citrated ox plasma
Foster (1942)	,,　,,　,,
Kuizenga, Nelson and Cartland (1943)	Citrated sheep plasma

Oxalated plasma + Ca-salt + tissue extract in excess.

MacIntosh (1941)	Oxalated horse plasma

Bird plasma + tissue extract.
Fischer and Schmitz (1932)
Chargaff, Bancroft and Stanley-
  Brown (1936)
Astrup (1938)
Jaques and Charles (1941)

The use of whole blood.

The cat method.

Howell determined the anticoagulant activity of his preparations of heparin on cat blood obtained from the carotids. A definite amount of blood was poured into tubes containing heparin and the tubes were kept on ice at 0° C. Readings were made after 24 hours. As previously stated, 1 milligram of his purest preparation of heparin kept 100 ml. of cat's blood from coagulating for 24 hours.

His method was modified by Charles and Scott (1944) and has been described as used in the routine assaying of heparin in the Connaught Laboratories by Jaques and Charles (1941) as follows:

"Carefully selected 8 mm. Widal tubes marked at a volume of 1 ml. are used. The tubes are grouped according to the bore, and only those of one group are used in one set of assays. A standard heparin solution containing 0.025 mg./ml. (2.5 units/ml.) of the crystalline barium salt of beef heparin is used. All solutions are made up in 0.85 per cent saline solution containing 0.3 per cent of tricresol. The unknown solution is diluted to approximately the same strength as the standard, as indicated by a preliminary assay. Four dilutions of the unknown in this range are taken, such that there is a difference of 10 per cent between each dilution. 0.1 ml., 0.2 ml., 0.3 ml. of each solution (the standard and four dilutions of the unknown) are measured into each group of three tubes and the volume is adjusted to 0.3 ml. with normal saline solution. These are placed in a rack holding 18 tubes. A cat is anaesthetised by intraperitoneal injection of amytal, one carotid artery is exposed and a clean glass cannula is inserted. The tubes are then filled to the 1 ml. mark with blood from the cannula. All the tubes in the rack containing only 0.1 ml. of the solutions are filled first, then those with 0.2 ml. and then those with 0.3 ml. The standard solutions are taken first, then the strongest dilutions of the unknown followed by other dilutions in order. As each tube is filled, it is mixed by inverting twice in such a manner that the blood covers the inside area of the tube. Three such racks may be filled at the same time, but each must have its own standard and be filled separately. The racks are placed in a water bath at 25° C. for two hours and the tubes are covered to prevent evaporation. Since occasionally all the tubes will be clotted after two hours, it is advisable to inspect the tubes after an hour and a half, and if all the tubes of the weakest dilution appear to be almost completely clotted, to read the tubes then; such a condition is readily seen, since settling of the red cells with the resultant buffy coat can normally be observed, whereas, if the blood is clotting too rapidly, this does not occur. The tubes are read by tipping each tube and judging the degree of clotting. A complete clot which does not break up on tipping is recorded as +, whereas completely fluid blood is recorded as —. Intermediate stages representing decreasing degrees of coagulating may be designated by D+, D, dd, d. At least four intermediate stages can be distinguished, and with practice, eight can be detected. After completing the reading the data are examined to compare the standard with the unknown. In a good assay the readings for the tubes containing the standard should match with those for one dilution of the unknown. The ratio of the potency of the unknown to that of the standard is as the respective dilutions of the two. Where the readings of the standard lie between those of two of the dilutions it is possible to estimate the potency of the unknown but where they lie beyond those of any of the dilutions of the unknown, it is necessary to make further assays using new dilutions of the unknown.''

The use of fresh beef blood.

The present author, in applying the original Howell method, used fresh beef blood as obtained directly from the blood vessels of the animals at the abattoir (Jorpes 1935, Wilander 1938, Jalling, Jorpes and Lindén, 1946). The last named authors described the method as follows.

"The coagulation time is determined in non-paraffined test tubes of pyrex glass holding 2.5 ml. ($70\times$ 8 mm.) without the admission of air. Ten tubes are placed in an oak rack ($30\times4\times2$ cm.), supplied with a cover of the same size. The lower side of the cover is faced with rubber as is also the upper surface of the rack so that all the tubes can be tightly closed at the same time. Since the exclusion of air is essential, the hinge and the metal hook closing the stand must be strongly fixed. In order to be able to close the stand tightly after filling, it is also equipped with a screwing device in the middle.

Each tube contains 0.2 ml. of a diluted heparin solution and a glass bead, of somewhat smaller size than the bore of the tube. Five of the tubes contain the standard heparin, five the unknown. The diluted solutions of standard heparin contain in the first tube 10 mg. of water-free substance per 32 ml. of physiological saline, in the second 5 mg. and so on. Corresponding dilutions of the unknown are made. In the summer the same amount of heparin is dissolved in 16 ml., during the winter sometimes in 64 ml.

When the animals are slaughtered at the abbatoir the blood is run directly from the carotid artery into a paraffined dish. Treatment of the dish with paraffin is in fact not essential.

One after the other, the tubes are quickly filled with blood, the cover then being tightened without allowing any air to enter the tubes, and the stand turned over several times. Mixing is obtained by means of the glass bead.

A thorough mixing is important before the stands

are left. Only two stands can be filled with blood from one dish. The first reading is made at the laboratory two hours later and sometimes even this reading is not used in the calculations. The readings made after 4, 8, 16 and 24 (26) hours give, in fact, the best results.

Since the slowing up of the speed of the glass bead indicates the beginning of coagulation the time for the initial coagulation is noted as well as that of the final stage. Tubes containing air bubbles are discarded.

The evaluation of the readings is an empirical one according to the following schema:

If standard and unknown are equal . 0
If one tube more is coagulated on the
   side of the standard . . . . . . +1
If two tubes more are coagulated on the
   side of the standard . . . . . . +2
If one tube more is coagulated on the
   side of the unknown . . . . . . — 1
If two tubes more are coagulated on the
   side of the unknown . . . . . . — 2

Initial coagulation ( ) is counted as half of full clotting. For instance, two clotted tubes on the side of the unknown against two fully clotted tubes and one partly clotted ( ), on the side of the standard means +0.5; or one clotted tube on the side of the unknown against two fully clotted and one partly clotted tube on the side of the standard means +1.5.

For every reading, after 4, 8, 16 and 24 (26) hours respectively, a figure is noted, thus four for every stand. All the figures obtained are added together and the sum divided by the number of readings.

The mean figure thus obtained is transposed into per cent of the standard in the following way:

$$— 1 \ = \ 50 \text{ per cent}$$
$$— 0.5 = \ 75 \text{ per cent}$$
$$0 \ = 100 \text{ per cent}$$
$$+ \ 0.5 = 150 \text{ per cent}$$
$$+ \ 1 \ = 200 \text{ per cent}$$

Above zero the mean figure ×100 is simply added to 100 per cent, below zero the mean figure is first divided by two before multiplying by 100 and subtracting it from 100 per cent.''

In this method the disturbing influence of the citrate and an unphysiological calcium ion concentration on the blood proteins is eliminated. The temperature need not be regulated since its influence is the same on both the standard and the unknown. Samples varying two hundred per cent in strength can be compared with each other. As no experimental animals are necessary the cost of an assay is minimal. The accuracy of the method is about 5 per cent.

A detailed description of a similar method using *rabbit blood taken from the carotid artery* through a cannula and giving an error of less than 10 per cent was published by F. Schütz in 1941.

The use of heparinized plasma and kinase.

Dam and Glavind (1939) *used the mutual neutralizing effect of heparin and thrombokinase.* A human brain extract was added to plasma from heparinized human whole blood in an amount just sufficient to neutralize the heparin and give a coagulation of the plasma in 3 minutes. Only heparin, no synthetic anticoagulant, could be used as reference substance.

The use of citrated or oxalated blood.

Because of the difficulty of getting and handling fresh blood, oxalated or citrated blood is used in most of the laboratories. The coagulation time is determined in the presence of heparin either after recalcification of citrated ox plasma (Reinert and Winterstein 1939, Foster 1942, Jores and Detzel 1940) or of citrated sheep plasma (Kuizenga, Nelson and Cartland 1943), or after adding a thrombin solution to oxalated ox plasma (Jaques and Charles 1941). The use of thrombin, which is partly neutralized by the heparin, allows the readings to be made after 15 minutes.

For the purpose of accelerating the reaction an excess of kinase has also been added to the oxalated horse blood simultaneously with the calcium (MacIntosh 1941 a).

The thrombin method.

The use of *oxalated beef blood and thrombin* markedly improves the sharpness of the end-point and may be found more convenient in some laboratories. The thrombin solution is standardized by adding varying amounts to a clotting system composed of 0.5 ml. of blood, 0.1 unit of heparin, and normal saline solution to give a total volume of 1.0 ml. and examining the tubes after they have been standing fifteen minutes at 25° C. That amount of thrombin which is just sufficient to cause clotting is then taken for the assay. The stock thrombin solution is diluted as required to contain this amount of thrombin in 0.1 ml. For the assay, a 0.4 unit per ml. of solution of the heparin standard is used and 0.20, 0.22, 0.25, 0.27, 0.32 ml. taken in carefully selected tubes (as described for the Howell method). For maximum accuracy, tubes with volumes between these may also be taken. The volume is made up to 0.4 ml. with saline and 0.5 ml. of oxalated beef blood is added. In another series of tubes equivalent amounts of the unknown, as found by preliminary assay, are taken. The tubes are allowed to stand in a water-bath at 25° C. for exactly ten minutes to come to temperature equilibrium and then 0.1 ml. of the thrombin is added to each tube, the system being mixed immediately by inverting the tube twice. The tubes are allowed to stand in a constant temperature water-bath at 25° C. for fifteen minutes and then read. Below a certain concentration, which is the end-point, the clot breaks up, and with higher concentrations, of course, no clot is formed. The end-point will be found between one pair of tubes.

The reagents are prepared as follows: Beef blood is collected in 1 litre flasks containing 10 ml. of 20 per cent neutral potassium oxalate. The blood is obtained from a cannula in the carotid artery. Where it is not possible to obtain blood in this manner, mixed venous blood from the abattoir may be used. This blood does not give as sharp an end-point and requires less thrombin than the arterial blood. Oxygenation of the venous blood has no effect on this difference. The blood is stored in the ice chest and keeps for about three weeks, at the end of which time the end-point of the assay begins to lose its sharpness. Every few days the blood is strained through a double layer of cheese-cloth to eliminate small clots which may seriously interfere with pipetting. This procedure appears to sharpen the end-point. The *thrombin* is prepared by the method of Mellanby, and the dry powder is stored in a desiccator in the ice-box. It retains its potency for years. As required, 500 mg. of the thrombin is extracted with 50 ml. of normal saline solution (containing 0.3 per cent of tricresol) at 25° C. for an hour, the reaction being kept between pH 7 and pH 8 by adding solid sodium carbonate. The extract is then cleared by centrifugation and stored in the ice-box. After two or three days its potency reaches a steady value and is constant for about a month. It is interesting that the potency increases markedly during the first two days. The flask is kept in ice water whenever it is taken out of the refrigerator. The standard heparin must be in the form of the sodium or ammonium salt.

Recalcification of citrated beef or sheep plasma.

A detailed description of the method applied by *Reinert and Winterstein* is given by *Foster*. Samples of heparin of different purity are assayed against a standard heparin. For details of the technique and the evaluation of the results, reference is made to the original paper of Foster. His statements about the working principles have general application to all the methods in use in this field: "There is probably no other biological assay in which greater care must be exercised to obtain consistent results. The utmost uniformity of manipulative procedure must be maintained at all times. This applies to the cleaning of the tubes and burettes as well as to exactness in measuring volumes, accuracy in preparing solutions, and the maintainance of constant time intervals for each step from start to finish.''

Kuizenga, Nelson and *Cartland* (1943) found *citrated sheep plasma* to have several advantages. It gave, in contradistinction to cat blood and oxalated beef and horse plasma, a sharp border between fluid and clot and a very firm clot in less than three minutes after recalcification, thus making the addition of thrombokinase, as applied by MacIntosh to horse blood, unnecessary. Dilutions of the standard and two unknown heparin samples were assayed simultaneously in parallel rows. To 0.3 ml. of physiological saline solution containing 1.2, 1.4, 1.6, 1.8, 2.0 and 2.2 units of heparin in different tubes 1 ml. of citrated sheep plasma was added. Then 0.1 ml. of a 2 per cent calcium chloride solution was added, each tube closed with a paraffined cork and inverted 3 times. Readings were made after one hour at room temperature. The error of the method was less than 10 per cent.

The addition of kinase together with the calcium as recommended by MacIntosh introduces a serious source of error in the method. Here the excess of thrombokinase, commonly used in the prothrombin methods, will react with the heparin and remove at least part of it from the system, a drawback more pronounced in using less soluble heparin salts. Thus barium salts, because of the easy precipitability of the barium thrombokinase heparin complex, give too low figures with this method, as was found on repeated occasions by MacIntosh himself. The natural heparin, in contradistinction to the synthetic heparin preparations, was found by T. Astrup and co-workers (1944) to be very sensitive to thrombokinase. Dam and Glavind founded their method of assay on this reaction.

The use of the hen plasma — chicken embryo system.

Fischer and Schmitz reported in 1932 and Astrup in 1938 the extensive use of hen plasma, which keeps in the cold without any anticoagulants, and standardized thrombokinase preparations of chicken embryo. A linear relation is obtained between the heparin concentration and the log of the clotting time if the conditions are kept strictly standardized. The same principles were used by Chargaff, Bancroft and Stanley-Brown in 1936.

The advantages of *the methods based on the use of fresh whole blood* for the assay of heparin were discussed by Jalling, Jorpes and Lindén. Since heparin exerts a multiple effect on the blood, acting both on the thrombokinase and on the prothrombin and particularly strongly on the thrombin, the whole blood methods offer a better opportunity for heparin to exert its multiple effect than the methods based on the use of single components, the thrombokinase or the thrombin alone. The unfavourable influence of citrate and of an unphysiological concentration of calcium ions is also avoided.

Physico-chemical methods.

The anticoagulant activity of heparin preparations must be measured in biological systems. No physico-chemical or colour reaction will give reliable results. Thus the influence upon the iso-electric precipitability of proteins (Fischer 1931, 1935) as measured in the flocculation reaction of casein at its iso-electric point (Fischer and Schmitz 1932) is due to the acidic properties of the polysaccharide only. The same is the case with the precipitability with protamine (Chargaff and Olson) and with toluidine blue (Wilander 1938 a and MacIntosh 1941 b). The metachromatic colour reaction given by heparin with this dye is common to all polysaccharide sulphuric esters. As there is no close relationship between the biological activity and the degree of esterification of the polysaccharide fractions, particularly if heparin from different animals is compared, these physico-chemical methods are not very likely to give reliable results. In the presence of proteins or mucoproteins, as in urine, they are still less applicable. The quantitative determination of heparin in its natural *milieu* is therefore an almost impossible task.

The Heparin Standard.

The different principles which have been applied by different workers to express the anticoagulant activity of heparin are almost as many as the authors themselves.

Charles and Scott in 1933 determined the cat unit, originally suggested by Howell. One unit was the amount which prevented the coagulation of 1 ml. of cat blood kept for 24 hours at 0° C. One milligram of the pure heparin contained about 500 units.

Other units have been recommended by Schmitz (1935), by Chargaff, Bancroft and Stanley-Brown (1936), by de Puoz (1938), by Reinert and Winterstein (1939), by Astrup (1938) and by Jores.

Schmitz suggested as a unit the amount of heparin, one-thirtieth of which doubled the logarithm of the coagulation time in 0.1 ml. of hen plasma. Chargaff, Bancroft and Stanley-Brown also used hen plasma and a muscle kinase of standard potency as suggested by Fischer and Schmitz (1932). They defined an inhibitor unit which was very small, one-fifteenth of the original Howell unit.

de Puoz, and Reinert and Winterstein of the Hoffman-La-Roche laboratory expressed the potency of the heparin in anticoagulant units (a. c. u.). One a. c. u. keeps one ml. of recalcified citrated beef plasma uncoagulated at 37° C. for four hours. The necessary amount of calcium is to be titrated for each plasma specimen separately. One milligram of their pure heparin contained 500 a. c. u.

Realizing the impossibility of defining with accuracy an anticoagulant unit in terms of its action in any coagulation system, Bergström, Jorpes and Wilander (1937) tried to avoid reference to any kind of unit by expressing the anti-coagulant activity in milligrams of a standard heparin. For various reasons the sodium salt of the protein-free heparin polysaccharide from ox liver was selected for this purpose.

Heparin, as obtained by the routine method from ox liver, has, in fact, a very constant activity. As the preparation of stronger samples necessitates a fractionation of the barium or brucine salts with subsequent removal of barium and brucine, the starting material, which is non-toxic, was assumed to become the product to be used clinic-ally. This preparation of ox liver heparin has since then been used as standard in all clinical and scientific records made by Swedish workers. The amount of heparin given has been expressed only in milligrams.

In 1938 Murray and Best made the suggestion that the barium salt of the purest ox heparin, at that time assumed to be crystalline, should be accepted as standard, the unit being 1/100 of a milligram of that preparation. The activity of the corresponding sodium and ammonium salts and the free acid would consequently be 120, 127 and 156 units per mg. respectively. This unit has in the meantime been maintained as the Toronto unit and was in 1942 accepted as *the provisional international heparin unit.* As a refer-ence substance a water-free sodium salt of heparin obtained from a highly active barium salt was chosen, one unit being 1/130 of a milligram of the sodium salt.

The Swedish standard heparin contains 80 units per mg. of that strength as assayed with the ox blood method.

The commercial heparin samples outside Scandinavia are usually declared to contain 1000 units (10 mg.) or 5000 units (50 mg.) per ml. Thus a simplification is achieved, facilitating the practical use of heparin, a simplification which should be still more valuable, if the two unnecessary noughts at the end of the figures could be left out. In the clinics, 50—100—150 milligrams of heparin are ordinarily administered at a time, figures which are *per se* large enough without multiplying them by 100 or 500 as would be necessary if the provisional international heparin unit or the Roche anticoagulant unit were to be used.

The Strength of Pure Heparin *in Vitro.*

Tables X and XI give an approximate estimation of the anticoagulant activity of the standard heparin from beef liver if added to blood in open vessels or closed glass tubes respectively. Thus 1.5 mg. of heparin per litre of blood exerts a measurable influence on the coagulation time. The second table gives the mean values of a series of assays with the routine method during a period of two years.

TABLE X

The Coagulation Time, in Hours, for Human and Rabbit Blood Respectively at Room Temperature in an Open, Non-paraffined Vessel

Mg. of standard heparin per 100 ml. of blood				
0.5		1		2	3
Small clots	Coagulation	Small clots	Coagulation	Small clots	Small clots
$^1/_2$	$^1/_2-3$	$^1/_2-^3/_4$	$1\,^1/_2-6$	$1\,^1/_2$	6

TABLE XI

Coagulation Time, in Hours, of Ox Blood at Room Temperature, in Closed, Filled, Non-paraffined Glass-Tubes

	1.2	0.6	0.3	0—15
Mg. of heparin per 100 ml. of blood				
Time of coagulation	12—24	4—8(6)	$1\,^1/_2-3(2)$	$^1/_2-1$

In these standardizations the results showed a clear difference at different seasons of the year. In the summer the coagulation tendency was at least twice as great as during the winter.

Horse and dog blood gave the same results. There is no fundamental quantitative difference in this respect between the animals most commonly used for experimental purposes. The rapid coagulation in rats and mice may possibly depend on the production of kinase caused by the difficulties in obtaining the blood.

In this connection the treatment of the blood is a detail of great importance. The above-mentioned figures refer to blood running in a stream from the blood vessel without any considerable formation of kinase before being mixed with the heparin.

Apparently it is difficult to determine what quantity of heparin is necessary to maintain the fluidity of a certain amount of blood at room temperature. It may be said, however, that 1 mg. of heparin of standard potency in an ordinary open glass vessel at room temperature completely inhibits the coagulation of 10—20 ml. of blood.

The Effect of Heparin on Intravenous Administration.

In his very first papers Howell proposed that heparin be used for intravenous injection into animals in order to facilitate operative procedures, and since then heparin has been used for that purpose. It has proved to be a valuable aid when perfusing isolated organs, in crossed circulation, in blood-pressure experiments, etc. For these various purposes it has been found more suitable than all other anticoagulants, as it has turned out to be non-toxic.

Howell used his purified heparin for blood transfusions in man. There also exist reports on the use of heparin in long experimental series in man. G. Haas, in 1928, heparinized a patient by repeated intravenous injection of Heparin Promonta. In this nephritic patient with a high non-protein nitrogen a 'Blutwaschung' was brought about by letting the blood on its way from the radial artery to the cubital vein pass through a collodion loop immersed in Ringer's solution. A vivi-diffusion similar to that introduced by Abel into experimental physiology took place through the collodion membrane. The experiment could be carried out on heparinized human beings only, as all other anticoagulants such as hirudin, Germanin, salvarsan and Liquoid Roche were too toxic. In Haas's experiment the renal function in uraemia was assisted in this manner.

Heparin could not, however, be used extensively in man in such conditions owing to the low degree of purity. The injections were often followed by chills and fever, and the high price of the preparation also rendered its use impractical.

This aspect of the problem was somewhat changed when pure heparin was obtained. Even if given intravenously and repeatedly over a long period of time, the pure preparation produced no untoward effects, and more extended medical use could now be considered.

When given intravenously heparin has an almost immediate and relatively temporary effect. The intensity and duration of the action vary according to the dose. Apart from individual variations, which may be quite large, the effect is fairly similar in different kinds of animals, such as dogs, cats and rabbits. The threshold dose is seen from Fig. 9 to lie at 0.25 mg. per kilo of body-weight. The figure

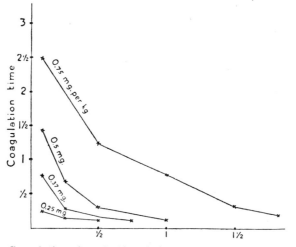

Fig. 9. Coagulation time (ordinate) in hours as influenced by small intravenous injections of heparin into rabbits.
Abscissa: time of sampling.

also demonstrates the rapidity with which the effect recedes after the various doses.

The same result, the curve being similar and of the same height, was obtained by Gross in 1928 upon injecting corresponding doses of a heparin preparation which was one-tenth as strong.

Small doses give approximately the same reaction in man. An injection of 7.5 mg. of standard heparin in young persons of normal weight caused no increase in the coagulation time. Injection of 15 mg. resulted in the practically normal coagulation time of 7—9 minutes. After 20 mg. there was a slight indication of effect, for the coagulation time was 15, 19, 11, 11, and 7 minutes in five different persons. The coagulation time was determined with the aid of a movable bead in filled, non-paraffined glass tubes at room temperature, according to Hedenius (1936 a).

In contrast to the synthetic anticoagulants, even strong intravenous doses of heparin cause no internal haemorrhage either within the organs or into the serous cavities of healthy animals. Cellulose trisulphuric acid, on the other hand, is very toxic (Bergström) and causes pleural and renal haemorrhages. Rabbits can stand repeated intravenous doses of 500 mg. of heparin without inconvenience. In a series of rabbits injected with 10 mg. of heparin per kilo of bodyweight intravenously four times daily for 10 days, no pathological changes whatsoever could be observed on histological examination of the parenchymatous organs.

The purified preparations give no toxic reaction whatever in dogs. Less pure, though highly active, preparations may, however, sometimes cause fever and chills in man.

Heparin is the ideal anticoagulant in animal experiments, as it has no toxic effect on the animals and no influence on blood-pressure or cardiac activity (Reed 1928—29). According to Kahlson and Landby (1937) the dose may be ten times larger than necessary without producing any inconvenience in these respects. They found heparin to be the only substance that can be used in experiments on guinea pigs without any untoward symptoms.

Even though it possesses advantages as a natural anticoagulant, it may very well be replaced by Chlorazol Fast Pink (Benzoechtrosa) in experiments on dogs, cats, and rabbits.

Other Similar Anticoagulants.

During the past few years a *new group of anticoagulants* has been used in animal experiments. They are strongly acidic organic compounds of a comparatively high molecular weight. Attention was focused on them by an observation made by Rous, Gilding and Smith in 1930. When studying the permeability of the capillaries to Chicago-blue 6 B, they found it inhibited coagulation.

This dye, No. 518 in the Colour Index, is a sodium salt of dimethyl-diphenyl-disazo-bis-8-amino-1-naphthol-5 : 7-disulphonic acid. Its action on coagulation was studied in detail in 1932 by Huggett and Silman and by Huggett and Rowe in 1934. The latter found another azo-dye, Chlorazol Fast Pink KBS No. 353 in the Colour Index, to be a still more suitable anticoagulant because of its greater activity and its lack of toxicity. This was later marketed in Germany under the name of Benzoechtrosa. It is a sodium salt of 3:5-disulpho-diphenylurea-4:4-disazo-bis-2-amino-8-naphthol-6-sulphonic acid. Huggett and his co-workers found that these dyes interfere in the first phase of coagulation by preventing thrombin formation. They were supposed to change the physico-chemical state of the prothrombin, making its activation impossible. These authors found that small details in the chemical structure have a decided influence on the action of these azo-dyes on coagulation.

Kahlson and Landby (1937) made a detailed study of the usefulness of these substances in experimental physiology.

It is noteworthy that a synthetic dye is so free from toxic secondary effects that Huggett and Silman could give intravenous doses of up to 300—500 mg. per kilo in rabbits. Apart from the disadvantage of the colour, Chlorazol Fast Pink would appear to have one advantage over heparin. In spite of heavy doses the blood of heparinized animals may coagulate in narrow vessels and in long narrow glass tubes, a drawback said to occur less frequently in experiments in which Chlorazol Fast Pink has been used. The failures in the heparin experiments are easily explained. The blood is injured by the surface effect of the glass or by the alkali it may release, and great quantities of thrombokinase are liberated from the thrombocytes. It is the same phenomenon that Lampert (1931) endeavoured to counteract in transfusion technique by the introduction of amber vessels (Athrombit) with needles of V 2 A-steel, a material which, like the American Lucite,[1] has a low surface affinity for both water and blood.

The rapidity of the excretion and the activity curve are about the same for this dye as for heparin. Owing to the discoloration produced there can be no question of using this substance to retard coagulation in man. There is a marked contrast between these azo-dyes and Liquoid Roche, Germanin, salvarsan, and neosalvarsan, the two latter of which have been used as anticoagulants. The latter have a very narrow margin between the intravenous effective dose and the dose which is toxic to the parenchymatous organs. Thus none of these substances can be used in man. Details of the toxicity of Liquoid Roche have been described by Demole and Reinert, 1930, Linkberg, 1932, M. Zunz, 1934, and by E. Zunz, 1934.

All have emphasized that on intravenous administration Liquoid Roche shows a very narrow margin between the effective and the lethal dose. It causes haemorrhages in the parenchymatous organs such as the kidneys, and can reduce the number of thrombocytes in the blood, as is also the case with salvarsan, neosalvarsan and Germanin. According to Stuber and Lang an intravenous injection of 750 mg. of Germanin in man causes a decrease in the thrombocytes of 7—60 per cent in 30—60 minutes.

Hirudin.

A physiologically interesting substance, occurring in the buccal glands of the leech, was discovered in 1884 by Haycraft. It was subjected to closer study by Franz 1902, at the pharmacological laboratory of Jacobi in Göttingen. The latter elaborated a method of preparation and suggested

---

[1] Lucite is a polymerized methyl methacrylate (Ind. Eng. Chem. 30. 8. 1938).

the name herudin or hirudin. The substance was supplied by E. Sachsse & Co. of Leipzig-Reudnitz. It was very expensive owing to the shortage of raw material. The chemical nature of its active component is unknown. The point of attack is unlike that of heparin in that it is supposed to inactivate thrombin as well as thrombokinase (Mellanby). *In vitro* hirudin is 30—50 times weaker than standard heparin. At one time, before the discovery of heparin, hirudin was the only anticoagulant used intravenously in animals. In spite of the high price it rendered valuable service to physiologists.

Novirudin.

A substitute for hirudin was introduced by Loeffler in 1926 from Jacobi's Institute, now in Tübingen. The new substance was called novirudin and is a sodium salt of humic acid. In 1922 Adler and Wiechowski had found that melanins obtained by oxidation of such substances as peat, charcoal and naphthalene inhibited coagulation of the blood. Loeffler discovered that melanins from tyrosine, naphthalene, and humic acid of plant materials were most effective. One milligram of these inhibited coagulation in 1 ml. of blood which could not be induced to clot even with tissue juices. Novirudin had an injurious effect on blood-pressure (Vartiainen, 1929) and cardiac activity (Kahlson and Landby 1937).

The availability of pure heparin has made both hirudin and novirudin superfluous.

Synthetic heparin preparations.

Synthetic polysulphuric acids of cellulose and of chondroitin sulphuric acid were prepared by P. Karrer and his co-workers in 1943 and 1944 by means of chlorosulphonic acid and pyridine, as done by Bergström in 1936 and by Chargaff and co-workers in the same year. The products were highly toxic. The toxic effect was reduced if an acid component was introduced in the polysaccharide molecule prior to the esterification. Thus the ether of cellulose with glycolic acid

$C_6H_9O_4 \cdot O \cdot CH_2COOH_x$ or with oxyethanolsulphonic acid $C_6H_9O_4 \cdot O \cdot CH_2CH_2SO_2OH_x$ was prepared and further esterified to polysulphuric acids in the ordinary way. The corresponding compounds relating to chondroitin sulphuric acid were also prepared. The sodium salts of these compounds were about seven times weaker than the commercial standard heparin. They exerted, however, *in vivo* a more prolonged action than heparin. They were still too toxic for intravenous use in man.

These polysulphuric acids behaved like heparin on fractionation of the brucine salt in water. The less soluble fractions showed the highest sulphur content and the strongest anticoagulant activity. There was no relationship, however, between the molecular structure of these synthetic anticoagulants as expressed in the viscosity of their solutions and their anticoagulant activity.

Similar synthetic experiments were performed by Astrup, Galsmar and Volkert (1944). The anticoagulant effect of cellulose trisulphuric acid and chitin disulphuric acid, studied by Piper (1945), was *in vivo* of about the same order as that of heparin. The *in vitro* effect on a chicken plasma—chicken embryo kinase system was quite different, the synthetic products being much less sensitive than heparin to an excess of thrombokinase. The synthetic products were all toxic. Given by mouth, they were not taken up by the intestine.

In a concentration of 0.1 per cent the cellulose trisulphuric acid precipitated fibrinogen at neutral reaction, whereas other plasma proteins were precipitated first on the acid side of their iso-electric point.

On intravenous administration the cellulose trisulphuric acid and the other synthetic products caused a very strong reaction on the thrombocytes, which immediatedly agglutinated. The thrombocytes were greatly reduced in numbers as a result of a filtering off of the agglutinated cells through the natural filters of the blood, mainly in the lungs. The thrombocytopenia which 30 minutes after injection of 1 mg. of chitindisulphuric acid ranged about 10,000 per mm^3, receded in 1—3 hours.

The cellulose trisulphuric acid in a concentration down to 0.000005 per cent caused an agglutination of the thrombocytes *in vitro*, a reaction not given by the natural heparin. *There was in this respect a marked difference between the natural and synthetic heparin preparations.*

A series of synthesis experiments were also performed by von Kaulla (1945), the best results being obtained with a xylane polysulphuric ester.

CHAPTER V

Miscellaneous Clinical Uses of Heparin.

Heparin as an Anticoagulant in the Examination of Blood.

Heparin came into use early in the study of blood. It was found to be very useful because it did not exert any osmotic action on the blood corpuscles. Although it carries a strong electric charge, it has a low osmotic pressure in aqueous solution. This detail is of great importance in the practical use of heparin. The low osmotic pressure, combined with the high activity, results in the elimination of all osmotic effects.

Even in a concentration of 1—2 pro mille the oxalates cause a shrinking of the blood corpuscles with the release of water. This increases the plasma volume and decreases the concentration of the plasma components by a few per cent. The influence of the oxalates on the volume of the blood corpuscles is shown in Table XII. In oxalate plasma Schmidt, in 1935, found a 4—12.5 per cent lower phosphatide content than in heparin plasma. The same is true of the other constituents of the plasma. Consequently analysis of, for instance, plasma lipoids can be carried out only with heparinized blood (Sperry and Schoenheimer 1935, Schmidt 1935, Gardner, Gainsborough and Murray 1938). In an extensive investigation on various anticoagulants (oxalates, citrate, Liquoid Roche, heparin, hirudin) in blood analyses, Blitstein, in 1935, demonstrated the great advantages of heparin. He found that oxalates and citrate cannot be used for the analysis of plasma components. A similar statement was made by Lange (1946 p. 180). The figures found for the plasma components in using heparin are identical with those obtained with hirudin and on defibrinated blood (Boyd and Murray 1937).

This behaviour of the erythrocytes has been used by Neuwirth (1937) in order to prove the free and ready permeability of the human erythrocyte membrane for glucose. The shift of fluid from the cell is accompanied by a passage of glucose. The same does not occur with rabbit's blood.

These investigations were almost all made with the impure heparin preparations previously available on the market. Consequently pure heparin, which is 10 times stronger, will be of still greater value. Thanks to its great activity, the concentration need not exceed 0.1 pro mille, that is to say, 1 mg. is sufficient for 10 ml. of blood and usually for 20—30 ml. It neither influences the volume of the blood corpuscles nor interferes with the chemical analysis. It has no reducing power, and the low nitrogen content, 1.5—2 per cent, does not influence the non-protein nitrogen values. The use of heparin for all kinds of blood analyses, including morphological examination, will thus merely depend on its availability.

Haematocrite determinations.

The literature contains a statement by Ponder (1934) to the effect that heparin is not very suitable for haematocrite determinations, owing to the fact that small clots easily form in heparinized blood, thus increasing the haematocrite values and making the results unreliable. His observations were made with the old weaker preparations. The high haematocrite values do not, however, appear when a sufficient amount of pure heparin is used. Thus Enghoff (1938) found the same values with heparin as with Liquoid Roche, neither of which have any osmotic influence on the volume of blood corpuscles. On the other hand, he stated that the citrate values were 6—7 per cent and the oxalate values 5—6 per cent lower than the figures obtained when using heparin, all of which is in complete agreement with Blitstein's data. The substances in question were used by Enghoff in the following concentrations: heparin 0.02—0.03 per cent, Liquoid Roche 0.04 per cent, sodium oxalate 0.18 per cent, and citrate about ten times as much. One milligram of heparin was thus used for 3—5 ml. of blood. He

found the difference between the individual determinations
to be greater with heparin, e. g. 45.4 ± 0.11 $(\delta = 0.36)$, than
with citrate, when the corresponding mean value for the
same blood sample was 42.9 ± 0.05 $(\delta = 0.16)$. As is apparent from these figures, the accuracy of which is quite
sufficient, the disadvantage pointed out by Ponder is thus
no longer present. On the other hand, it is obvious that
citrate cannot be used because the mean value for it is 6—7
per cent too low. Table XII shows figures obtained from
blood filled into tubes with heparin dried on the walls, and
demonstrates that as small a dose as 1 mg. is sufficient for
10 ml. of blood, and that even if a ten times larger quantity
of heparin is used it does not influence the values. Even
such a low concentration of oxalate as 1 mg. per ml. causes
a shrinkage in the volume of the blood corpuscles, and if
the concentration were to be doubled or quadrupled the
results would be unreliable. It should be pointed out that
there is no reason to assume that heparin would facilitate
swelling of the blood corpuscles, for instance, by glycolysis.
Glycolysis is just as rapid in oxalated blood as in heparinized blood. It is not powerful enough to exert any influence.
All experience with pure heparin indicates that it is a
suitable anticoagulant when determining the volume of the
red blood cells. Its suitability for that purpose was pointed
out also by Sack in 1940.

TABLE XII

The Red Cell Volume of Human Blood Filled into Heparin Tubes
(Wilander 1938 b). (Blood volume 10 ml.)

Ordinary heparin tubes	5 % heparin solution			20 % potassium oxalate solution		
	0.05 ml.	0.1 ml.	0.2 ml.	0.05 ml.	0.1 ml.	0.2 ml.
45.7	46.5	46.5	46.5	45.5	43.5	40
49.7	50	50	49.5	47.5	46.2	..
46.5	..	..	..	44	40	37
45	..	..	..	44.5	42	38
43.2	..	..	..	41.2	39	37
47.5	..	..	..	45.2	44	39

Morphological and chemical analysis of the blood.

In view of the fact that heparinized blood may be considered as normal, it would appear possible to use it for every kind of blood analysis. The clinical technique for blood examinations has certain disadvantages. The specimen is withdrawn from the capillaries for the morphological examination as well as for the determination of the haemoglobin. Other punctures are made to study the blood-sugar, and intravenous technique is used to obtain the specimens for the sedimentation reaction, for non-protein nitrogen, calcium, uric acid, etc. Various sets of pipettes and diluting solutions must be prepared to examine the capillary blood and still others for the S. R. The very fact that all these analyses can be made on heparinized blood means that the contact with the patient can be limited to one single venipuncture. The suitability of heparinized blood for such a complete analysis has been demonstrated by Wilander (1938 b). As early as 1928 Reed was able to show that Howell's purified heparin did not influence ordinary analysis of the blood.

Blood drawn into 10 ml. tubes containing 1 mg. of dried heparin can be used for examination of the haemoglobin, the red (and white) blood corpuscles, the thrombocytes, the red cell volume, differential counts, blood-sugar, non-protein nitrogen, calcium, uric acid, phosphates, phosphatase, etc. All figures except those for the white blood corpuscles are identical with those obtained in the ordinary manner with capillary or oxalate blood. The analyses in question, except for the white cell count and the determination of the blood-sugar, the phosphates and phosphatase, could be made as late as 12 or 24 hours after the blood was drawn, a very important detail from a practical point of view. The white cell count should, if possible, be made within 2 hours, as these cells display a definite tendency to agglutinate and disappear when the heparinized blood is kept for some time. This heparinized blood, intended for complete analysis, can also be used for the sedimentation reaction, either directly or after the addition of isotonic citrate solution, as described later.

Witts, in 1940, found heparin blood very suitable for the ordinary routine analyses in the clinic.

In the routine bacteriological analysis the blood is aspirated into a 20 ml. syringe moistened inside with about 0.1 ml. of a 5 per cent heparin solution before mixing it with agar or broth. The formation of bacteria-enclosing fibrin clots is thereby prevented.

The absence of osmotic effect makes heparin particularly suitable when it is desirable to determine the resistance of the red blood cells. There are certain disadvantages connected with the use of oxalate blood.

Due to the great stability of heparin, a solution of the substance can be evaporated to dryness in tubes at 110° C., thus giving a film of heparin inside the tube. These tubes can also be sterilized at 170° C. in order to be used for bacteriological examination of the blood.

It should be pointed out that heparinized blood cannot be utilized for the Wassermann reaction, as the heparin binds complement and causes an inhibition of haemolysis. Nor is it possible to use heparin plasma for iso-agglutination experiments, as the iso-agglutinin titre is lowered by heparin.

The blood can also be heparinized by giving the patient an intravenous injection of 50—75 mg. of pure heparin, a possibility which may prove advantageous when a series of blood samples are to be taken one after the other. This method is certainly the most suitable when it is desired for analytical purposes to have the blood fluid in its natural state.

Heparin and the sedimentation reaction.

Heparin has also come into use in the testing of the sedimentation rate of the blood corpuscles. It was natural that this physiological anticoagulant would be tested and compared with the generally used citrate. The findings in this connection are of such great interest that they deserve special mention.

The sedimentation rate of the erythrocytes is determined by the physical condition of the plasma. It is influenced by the fibrinogen content of the plasma, a fact which was known early in the nineteenth century (Nasse 1836). It is markedly affected by the globulin content, or more correctly by alteration in the globulin-albumin ratio (Fåhraeus 1924). Increased rate of sedimentation is a very sensitive expression of humoral alterations in the blood. The sedimentation reaction has therefore become an indispensable clinical method of examination. Since the pioneer work of Robin Fåhraeus in 1921, extensive experience has been gained in connection with this reaction and its use in different pathological states (Reichel 1936).

In routine technique, as worked out by Westergren in 1920, a 3.8 per cent solution of tri-sodium citrate is added to the blood in the proportion of 1 volume to 4. This technique has been regarded as the most suitable for detecting pathological changes in the blood.

Chiefly on theoretical grounds, certain criticisms have, however, been brought forward. The citrate, like other salts, exerts an inhibitory effect on the natural course of sedimentation and might therefore be not altogether suitable.

The inhibitory effect of salts on the rate of sedimentation had been pointed out by Fåhraeus as well as by workers both before and after him. It was also known by Nasse. The addition of 5 mg. of NaCl to 1 ml. of defibrinated horse-blood altered the rate per 15 minutes in Fåhraeus's experiments from 75 to 3 mm. The phenomena were studied from a practical standpoint by Rourke and Plass in 1929. Fluorides, as well as oxalates and citrates, retarded the rate of sedimentation, and the delay was proportional to the increase in concentration.

Rourke and Plass were able to show that heparin had no influence on the rate of sedimentation of the red blood cells. An increase in its concentration did not alter the values. This feature was best demonstrated in blood from a haemophiliac with a coagulation time of more than 5 hours, where the addition of heparin had no influence on the sedimentation rate.

In an experimental study Enocksson (1931) showed the great influence of salts on suspension stability, particularly in pathologically altered blood. They are able to cause a marked disturbance in the natural course of sedimentation.

Enocksson, like Rourke and Plass, had an opportunity to study the influence of the addition of citrate and heparin to haemophilic blood on which the sedimentation rate can be read off directly without any anticoagulant. The results are to be found in Table XIII.

TABLE XIII

The Sedimentation Rate of Haemophilic Blood with and without Anticoagulants

	Sedimentation	
	in 30 min.	*in* 1 hr.
Without anticoagulant	6.5 mm.	17 mm.
With citrate according to Westergren	3.5 »	8 »
With heparin (syringe moistened with a 5 per cent solution).............	6.0 » 6.5 »	20 » 20 »
With heparin (syringe moistened with a 2.5 per cent solution)...........	5.5 »	16 »
With heparin as dry powder	7.0 » 5.5 »	21 » 16 »

It is evident that the addition of heparin has no influence, whereas the 3.8 per cent citrate (1 volume to 4 volumes of blood) reduces the rate of sedimentation. A similar observation on haemophiliacs was made by Ham and Curtis in 1938.

In a later study Enocksson and co-workers (1936) compared the sedimentation rate when citrate and heparin were used as anticoagulants. In the beginning they did not have a very pure preparation, but later they used the pure heparin. A study of Enocksson's large tables discloses that the citrate S. R. is considerably lower than the heparin S. R., except when the figures are low and normal. When the rate of sedimentation is normal, as in healthy subjects, the two methods give the same values, but as soon as the pathological limit has been passed the heparin S. R. gives higher figures in almost all cases.

This phenomenon can be interpreted as a result of the stabilizing influence of the salts, in this case of the citrate and sodium ions on the suspension stability of the blood, probably acting by way of the plasma proteins. The effect of the citrate is easy to demonstrate. If blood is drawn into a tube containing heparin as dry substance, the S. R. may be determined directly or 1/4 volume of 3.8 per cent citrate may first be added. The difference established by Enocksson is then beautifully demonstrated. The values obtained when the heparinized blood has been mixed with citrate are almost identical with those obtained in the ordinary manner according to Westergren (Table XIV, Wilander 1938 b).

It is apparent from the table that heparinized blood can be used for the S. R. for at least 2 hours after withdrawal, and possibly for as long as 6 hours.

The inhibition exercised by the salts can also be demonstrated without diluting the blood with a solution of citrate, if increasing quantities of common salt are added to a number of heparin tubes before the blood is added.

These findings demonstrate that salts, including sodium citrate, markedly upset the natural sedimentation rate of the blood corpuscles, and at the same time suggest that the rate of sedimentation obtained with heparinized blood may be the correct one, or that of the blood itself.

In addition to the already discussed, purely physiological advantages of the heparin sedimentation reaction there is also the ease with which it is carried out. Heparin blood can, for instance, be used directly for the sedimentation test. This gets rid of the difficulty of mixing blood and citrate in definite proportions without admitting any air. Also the greater sensitivity of the heparin sedimentation test may be an advantage in special cases.

These experimental studies naturally accentuate interest in the use of heparin when determining the S. R. However, experience up to the present would appear to indicate that its practical use presents not only advantages but also disadvantages, and its introduction into clinical routine is not so obviously indicated. The current citrate technique works

7

TABLE XIV

Sedimentation Rate for the 1st Hour for Heparinized Blood with and without Citrate, as Compared with the Figures of the Ordinary Westergren Technique (Wilander 1938 b).

Westergren's original technique after 1 hour	Heparinized blood with citrate				Heparinized blood without citrate			
	mixed immediately after bleeding	mixed 2 hours after bleeding	mixed 6 hours after bleeding	mixed 12 hours after bleeding	immediately after bleeding	2 hours after bleeding	6 hours after bleeding	12 hours after bleeding
1	1	1	1	1	2	2	1	1
1	1.5	2	2	1	2	3	2	1
4	5	5	6	3	10	6	7	7
8	8	6	10	14	12	..	..	22
10	10	11	11	..	13	17	18	..
16	19	19	19	16	23	4	19	14
17	19	19	18	16	28	31	21	22
18	20	18	17	12	38	36	28	13
19	30	20	27	29	15	13	3	20
24	26	25	22	25	47	43	36	43
24	23	24	22	22	24	..	..	41
29	29	32	30	29	24	45	47	28
31	38	40	43	35	35	50	30	7
34	37	37	26	21	66	69	46	37
36	37	36	30	29	52	55	48	45
39	37	37	39	27	..	..	..	33
50	49	50	46	33	75	68	70	51
74	73	70	72	79	48	29	13	1
85	86	80	74	74	58	58	45	45
107	109	111	109	81	109	106	108	94

precisely enough not to warrant the introduction of any better method. Moreover, due to the mass of clinical experience with the citrate technique (Reichel 1936), the method may be regarded as fully investigated. A change to a technique which gives other values would, therefore, present certain inconveniences.

The disadvantages of the heparin S. R. have been pointed out by Westergren 1937, 1938, Berseus 1938, and Ström 1938. The technique (1 mg. dried heparin for 10 ml. blood and the ordinary Westergren tubes) is hampered by an average error three times greater than with the citrate S. R. and is therefore less reliable. The mean error for the citrate S. R. was 5.4 per cent of the mean, and for the heparin S. R. 17.3 per cent (Ström). If, however, the citrate S. R. is done with heparin blood, the mean error becomes 6.4, which is practically the same as for the ordinary citrate S. R.

Ström, however, pointed out that the figures obtained by Wilander with citrated heparin blood were not identical with those obtained with citrate only. The differences between the two first columns of Table XIV are, however, so small that they are of no practical importance whatsoever. *Heparin does not disturb the sedimentation rate, if the heparinized blood is diluted with citrate solution.* The same was shown by Nielsen (1942) to be the case if the blood (four parts) is mixed with 0.5 to 0.7 per cent sodium chloride solution (one part) containing 1 pro mille of heparin. The accuracy and the final figures proved to be the same. Nielsen (1943) also obtained reliable results using a microtechnique with capillary tubes. He collected blood in heparinized tubes for ordinary routine analysis and later made the dilution with saline.

The preceding discussion refers to concentrations of 1 mg. of heparin in 5 to 50 ml. of blood, a concentration which need never be exceeded. If the heparin concentration is increased to 1 mg. or more per cubic centimetre of blood, the picture will be quite different (von Kaulla 1938, Sappington and Gillis 1941). The heparin effect on the ordinary blood proteins then comes into action and an altogether abnormal, usually too rapid, sedimentation takes place. This phenomenon, however, is of theoretical interest only.

Usually, 0.1—0.2 mg. of heparin is added to 1 ml. of blood. Either the syringe is moistened with 0.5 or 1 per cent heparin solution or the heparin is dried as a film inside the test tube to make 1 mg. per 6—10 ml.

In a very comprehensive treatise in 1942 Östner discussed the factors influencing the sedimentation rate in heparinized blood with and without citrate.

Micro-technique.

Magnusson and Ahnsjö made an attempt to work out a micro-technique for heparin using sedimentation tubes 2 mm. in diameter and 100 mm. long. Like all the other micro-methods this also turned out to be less reliable than the macro-citrate S. R. Too high values were often obtained without corresponding clinical evidence of disease (Magnusson 1938 a). On the other hand, the greater sensitivity of the method allowed the demonstration of subclinical infections in cases with a pathological white blood-cell picture and a normal ordinary citrate S. R. (Magnusson 1938 b).

Sappington and Gillis made use of Wintrobe tubes (5 mm./50 mm.), Cutler tubes (4 mm./100 mm.) and Westergren tubes (2.5 mm./200 mm.) and compared the heparin S. R. with the citrate and the oxalate methods. In general the heparin S. R. showed in both normal and pathological blood a more rapid rate of sedimentation, the difference being most marked with the Westergren technique. Contrary results were often obtained in pneumococcic pneumonia, the heparin S. R. showing the lower rate.

The practical value of the heparin S. R. was studied in 1940 by Vannfält in 60 patients with tuberculosis of the lungs. The figures obtained after one hour with heparin and with citrate in the ordinary Westergren tubes were compared on different occasions during the course of the disease. The clinical signs of improvement or exacerbation as evidenced by the temperature, the roentgenological picture and the bacillary findings in the sputum were followed. The heparin S. R. seemed to be quite as useful as the citrate S. R. and in many instances it responded more adequately to changes in the clinical picture.

Because of the high mean error of the heparin S. R. and the stabilizing influence of the citrate upon the sedimentation rate most authors agree with Hambleton and Christianson who stated in 1939 that the original Westergren technique is the most suitable for the sedimentation reaction. According to these authors all improvements in this technique, including the replacement of the citrate with heparin, only make the test more tedious and difficult to interpret without increasing its clinical value. They recommend the Westergren technique by reason of its simplicity, reliability and priority.

Heparin in Blood Transfusion.

Blood transfusions are performed in many different ways. Up to the present, citrate has been the only anticoagulant used.

Some workers, however, are of the opinion that the citrate method is not without disadvantages. Many point out that chills occur more often after citrate than after whole-blood transfusions. Thus, Schäffer of Vienna expressed himself decidely in favour of whole-blood transfusions, at least in paediatrics.

At least in giving rapid transfusions of large volumes of blood to man and animals there is a danger in giving citrated blood. Ivy and his co-workers (1943) found that dogs deprived of 45—65 per cent of their estimated blood volume without replacement died in 84 per cent. If citrated whole blood or plasma was given during 5 minutes to replace the loss 50 and 70 per cent respectively of the dogs died. With heparinized blood, however, only 6 per cent of the animals died. Ivy et al. concluded that 1,500— 2,000 ml. of citrated plasma given during a short time to a man could prove fatal. This question has been further studied by Thornton, Adams and Carlton (1945).

The transfusion of undiluted whole blood is recognized everywhere as the most suitable. Consequently numerous apparatuses have been constructed for this purpose (Beck, Unger, et al.). However, the transfusion of whole blood requires complicated appliances and technique. This is true of the routine introduced by Brown-Percy which requires a paraffined vessel, generally a Jeanbreau flask, and exposure and ligation of the veins of both subjects. Even the athrombit method of Lampert is rather complicated. The fixing of the needle of V 2 A steel to the amber vessel makes it more difficult to manage than when it is attached to a rubber tube.

All the above-mentioned methods are now of only historical interest.

Heparinization of the blood in vitro.

Experiments to replace the citrate by heparin were started by Sköld at St. Erik's Hospital in Stockholm in 1935, as soon as the pure heparin was obtainable. He describes his technique in the following manner.

20 mg. (0.4 ml. of 5 per cent solution) of heparin and a little sterile physiological saline solution are introduced into a sterile litre Erlenmeyer flask, or still better a round-bottomed flask supplied with a ground stopper. The quantity of blood required, about 500 ml., is drawn into the flask. After inserting the stopper with the necessary tubes the blood is pumped over to the recipient. The veins of donor and receiver are punctured with fairly fine needles. The blood vessels need never be exposed and ligated.

As the threshold dose in man is 0.25 mg. per kilo of body-weight, a dose of 20 mg. might be presumed to influence the coagulating time of the patient's blood. Experience has shown, however, that there is no danger of this. Lithander (1938) used the dose in question without complications when transfusing 5 cases of bled-out ulcer. The haemostyptic effect of the introduced blood appeared as usual. The bleeding time in open lesions in persons with a normal kinase system need not be prolonged even if the coagulation time has been influenced by the heparin. The tissue kinase at the site of the lesion inhibits the heparin effect. The coagulation time in venous blood and the bleeding time in minor lesions are not related to one another.

The bleeding time as determined by the Ivy technique remains normal in spite of an intensive heparinization (Lindgren and Wilander 1941, Ganes 1942).

Heparinization of the donor.

In studying the effect of heparin after intravenous administration in man, Hedenius arrived at a new transfusion technique. When once it had been found possible to heparinize man without any disadvantage, he suggested that blood transfusions be made from heparinized donors. The dose of heparin necessary, 1 mg. per kilo of body-weight, given 5 minutes before venesection, gives the donor's blood a coagulation time of 20—30 minutes. The quantity of heparin received by the patient, about 0.1 mg. per kilo of body-weight, is too small to influence his coagulation time, even if repeated transfusions are given.

The method is particularly valuable when the transfusion is to be done without assistance and with an inadequate apparatus.

It has been used by Crafoord in more than one thousand transfusions and is in general use at some clinics. In the case of routine donors sensitization might be expected to occur through repeated injections. Slight symptoms of that kind have been reported in a few donors, and these, have not been given heparin again.

These procedures for blood transfusions have also been used by Knoll and Schürch (1938) and by Sappington (1939) and found to be simple and valuable.

For venesection on patients with polycythaemia intravenous heparinization is very valuable. Without previous heparinization the flow of blood is very slow and the procedure of venesection tedious.

This principle of heparinizing the donor is of extraordinary value in all kinds of experiments using *crossed circulation in animals or man*. In fact, the accessibility of heparin is a prerequisite for the performance of many experiments in which the vascular system is involved, e. g. in *experiments with an artificial kidney* (Kolff 1944, 1946). The use of heparin also facilitates the technique of *measuring the arterial blood pressure* in animals where it is injected through the rubber tubing fixed to the glass cannula inserted into the carotid artery.

Heparin in the infusion technique.

Intravenous infusion is very often complicated by thrombosis or spastic contraction of the veins. This drawback is to a large extent eliminated by adding heparin to the infusion fluid. Martin (1944) suggested that heparin should be added to the liquid in all continuous infusions, 1 unit per ml. of solution or 1,000 units (10 mg.) per litre. He added also heparin to the citrate blood in blood transfusion, without leaving out the citrate. In giving penicillin intravenously in infusion a larger amount of heparin, 3 units per ml., is necessary.

Similarly Magnusson and Frisell (1947) gave glucose and amino acids together with penicillin and sulphonamides in intravenous infusion to infants and children with bacterial cerebrospinal meningitis and in cases of cholera infantum. Thus a child, weighing 16 kg., was given intravenously every third hour 50 ml. physiological saline containing 25 mg. heparin + 50 ml. casein hydrolysate + 50 ml. 5 per cent glucose and 20,000 units of penicillin. Simultaneously 5 ml. Elkosin (Ciba) were given intramuscularly. In the cases of cholera infantum treated in this way the excellent results were ascribed to the intravenous amino acid administration. For the intravenous infusion a silver cannula (Fig. 15) was inserted into a vein above the medial malleolus and left *in situ* for a week or more. Without heparin thrombotization of the vein followed in a short time.

CHAPTER VI

Dicumarol, the Haemorrhagic Agent Causing "Sweet Clover Disease".

History.

A new disease in cattle termed "sweet clover disease" was described in 1922—1923 by F. S. Schofield, a pathologist at the Ontario Veterinary College, Canada. In the winter of 1921—22 the district veterinarians had reported a new, usually fatal, disease in cattle. The animals died from excessive bleeding after trauma, dehorning, castration or parturition. The disease was thought to have some connection with the eating of spoiled hay from sweet clover. Schofield analyzed the syndrome of the disease and came to the conclusion that he was dealing with a condition not previously described. It bore a certain resemblance to haemorrhagic septicaemia, but there were no signs of inflammation in the internal organs. The course of the disease was also more rapid than in septicaemia. Haemorrhagic or oedematous swelling, extravasation of blood into the abdominal cavity, subperitoneal and subserous haematomata, and ecchymoses in the intestinal wall were common. Haemorrhages were always present in the liver. The bleeding tendency was the dominant feature in the syndrome. This tendency was believed by Schofield to be partly due to a defective clotting capacity owing to a deficiency, or an inhibition, of the thrombin. With regard to the cause, he said: "a powerful poison is most likely developed in the clover by microbiological activity". Schofield also succeeded in producing similar symptoms in rabbits fed with the same fodder.

Between 1928 and 1931, Roderick, at the North Dakota Agricultural Experiment Station, supplied an exhaustive account of the disease in numerous publications. Haemorrhage occurred in various parts of the body, under the epithelia and the serous membranes, in the ventricles of the brain, the walls of the bladder, the bone marrow, and more especially in the subcutaneous connective tissue and under the fasciae of the muscles. It was impossible to establish with certainty whether it was a question of genuine haemorrhage by diapedesis or whether some damage to the vessel wall was also present. No sign of the latter could be found in the animals upon postmortem examination. Contrary to the findings of Schofield, Roderick was unable to detect any degenerative lesions in the internal organs, in which the bleeding was otherwise moderate. In his opinion, the animals had died from bleeding. Albuminuria was only present when large quantities of blood appeared in the urine. In the liver only, he observed, microscopically, necrotic areas in about 50 per cent of the cases. He considered that the defect was to be sought in the blood chemistry, and he observed, as Schofield had done, that there were no noticeable changes in the composition of the blood other than the low prothrombin content.

Roderick, as well as other investigators, endeavoured in 1931, to extract the active agent with water, ethyl alcohol, ether, acetic acid, and other solvents, but without success. It was not until 1934, when experiments on a larger scale were carried out by a group of workers at the Wisconsin Agricultural Experiment Station (Campbell, Link and others), that better results were achieved. An extraction process was worked out during the years 1936 to 1937 (Roberts 1938). Water-soluble substances and lipoids were removed. The active principle still remaining in the hay was extracted with weak alkali and further purified by a rather complicated procedure. The activity was tested on rabbits (Campbell, Smith, Roberts and Link 1941), using Quick's method of prothrombin determination (Quick, Stanley-Brown and Bancroft 1935) and his experience in producing "sweet clover disease" in rabbits (Quick 1937).

Chemistry.

In September 1940, the active principle was obtained in a crystalline form (Campbell and Link 1941). It was weakly acid, and soluble in water only after the addition of alkali. Equivalent weight, 168. It was free from nitrogen, sulphur, and phosphorus, and was optically inactive. The empirical formula was $C_{19}H_{12}O_6$. With diazomethane a dimethyl ether was obtained.

The *chemical identification* of the substance (Stahmann, Heubner and Link 1941) was a fine piece of work. First it was proved that the substance was not identical with any of the sixty or so coumarin derivatives which had previously been isolated from nature. The formation of a diacetate and a dimethyl ether resistant to alkali, as well as a colour reaction with iron chloride, indicated the presence of two enolic hydroxyl groups. The hydroxyl groups were not phenolic. Keto groups were also observed. Fusion with KOH yielded 83 per cent of salicylic acid. Treatment with 30 per cent alcoholic KOH gave a diketone, $C_{17}H_{16}O_4$, which proved to be 1.3-disalicyllyl propane.

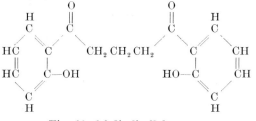

Fig. 10. 1.3-disalicyllyl propane.

On mild treatment, the yield of the latter was quantitative. With phenylhydrazine, a product with 9 atoms of carbon in addition to those in the phenylhydrazine was obtained. This indicated that the compound, with its 19 C atoms, might be composed of two C_9 substances of a ketone nature held together by a C atom. For various reasons it was supposed that the salicylic acid and the diketone originated from a chromane, 2.4 diketochromane, which is otherwise isomeric with, and can be transformed into the tautomeric 4-hydroxycoumarin (β-oxycoumarin).

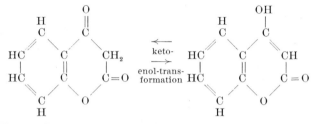

Fig. 11. Keto-enol-transformation from 2.4-diketo-chromane to 4-hydroxycoumarin.

The latter well-known compound, β-oxycoumarin, which was studied in particular by Anschütz in 1903, is known to be readily condensed with aldehydes such as formalin in the following manner:

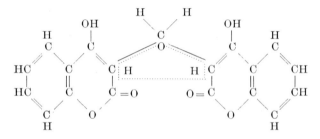

Fig. 12. The formation of 3.3'-methylene-bis-(4-hydroxycoumarin) or dicumarol.

The condensation product with formaldehyde α-methylene-bis-β-oxycoumarin was synthesized and described by Anschütz in 1909. The chemical properties and the physical constants of the haemorrhagic agent resembled those of the α-methylene-bis-β-oxycoumarin of Anschütz. When the latter compound, which was later called 3.3' methylene-bis-(4-hydroxycoumarin), was synthesized by Link and his collaborators, its physical constants were found to be identical with those of the haemorrhagic agent. The synthetic product was as biologically active as the natural product.

The identity of the two products was further confirmed by the common break-down products and common derivatives of these. This work was completed in November 1940 and was published in April 1941.

After the constitution of the compound had been eluci-dated by Link and his co-workers, the synthesis was clear. A simple method of producing benzotetronic acid (β-oxycoumarin) was described by Pauly and Lockemann in 1915. If acetyl salicylic acid methyl ester is fused with metallic sodium, 4-hydroxycoumarin is formed at 165° C. This, in its turn, is readily condensed with formaldehyde to 3.3'-methylene-bis-(4-hydroxycoumarin).

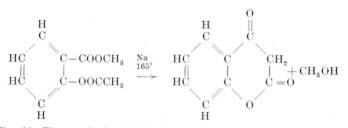

Fig. 13. The synthesis of 2.4-diketo-chromane from methyl ester of acetylsalicylic acid.

The application of this compound in clinical medicine will be discussed in a special chapter. (See Link 1944, 1945.)

PART II

Heparin and Thrombosis

CHAPTER VII

Heparin in the Treatment of Thrombosis.

The Proposed Use of Heparin in Thrombosis.

The coagulation of the blood plays an important rôle in the formation and growth of thrombi. Even if cellular processes participate in the matrix formation, the thrombocytes are soon enclosed in a network of fibrin (Fig. 14), which spreads along the vessels. Thus, if the mechanism of coagulation could be put out of action, the growth of a thrombus ought to be prevented. From a purely physiological point of view the addition of anticoagulants *in vivo* to the blood would therefore seem to be a specific treatment for thrombosis and pulmonary embolism. Heparin has consequently occupied a prominent position in the discussion of the prevention and treatment of thrombosis.

Now that heparin has become an important therapeutic substance, it is quite interesting to look back to 1917, the year after its discovery by Howell and McLean. In his Harvey Lecture of that year, Howell said: "We may hope, therefore, that these phosphatides, cephalin, causing an acceleration, and antiprothrombin, causing a retardation of the coagulation, will find a suitable application in experimental work and possibly in the therapeutic treatment of disorders of coagulation."

Since heparin was the only known physiological anticoagulant, the idea of using it in thrombosis was conceived at a very early stage. As mentioned above, Howell touched cautiously upon this problem as early as 1917, and he and MacDonald returned to it in 1930. They demonstrated that single injections in man and dogs had no injurious effect. In dogs the intravenous injection of Howell's purified

8

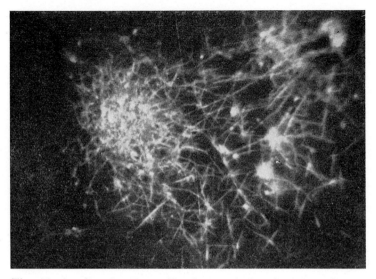

Fig. 14. A micro-thrombus with clumps of thrombocytes and a net of newly formed threads of fibrin.[1]

heparin for 6 days still caused no untoward symptoms. The heparin exerted no influence on the number of erythrocytes, leucocytes, or thrombocytes in the blood. The reduction of the coagulation time during the hours immediately following a heparin injection, observed earlier by Howell when using less pure preparations on dogs, was not noticed when using the purer product. As a result of their experiments, Howell and MacDonald, in 1930, recommended intravenous heparin treatment "in cases of venous thrombosis in man".

The harmlessness of the purified heparin had been thoroughly demonstrated by Reed (1928). In several hundred experiments on dogs heparin was injected intravenously in quantities up to 60 mg. per kilo without exerting any influence on the temperature, pulse rate, blood pressure, or reflex excitability.

---

[1] From "Die Thrombozyten des menschlichen Blutes" by Prof. Dr med. A. Fonio and Dr med. J. Schwendener. Medizinischer Verlag Hans Huber, Bern, Switzerland. Courtesy of the publisher.

In the following years Linkberg (1932), Zunz (1934) and Morawitz (1934) again discussed this question. Linkberg tried to use Liquoid Roche and Germanin to prevent post-operative thrombosis. They proved, however, to be toxic. Because of the difficulty of obtaining heparin, the idea of using this substance in thrombosis had also to be abandoned. In 1932 Morawitz, the Nestor in this field, described in Deutsche Gesellschaft für Kreislaufforschung the position as it stood at that time in the following way:

"We must frankly admit that we are almost as helpless as we were fifty years ago. In spite of numerous suggestions we have at present no reliable means for the prevention and treatment of thrombosis. Theoretically it would seem advantageous if thrombosis is imminent, e. g. after operations, to check the clotting of the blood. Thus Aschoff, de la Camp et. al. prevented the agglutination of thrombocytes to thrombi by making the blood incoagulable. So far, however, we have not succeeded in finding a suitable anticoagulant. Heparin is too expensive, Germanin too toxic and hirudin is both."

The Prevention of Thrombosis in Animal Experiments.

To demonstrate the usefulness of heparin in inhibiting thrombosis a series of animal experiments, initiated in 1932 in the Department of Surgery of the Toronto General Hospital, were performed in close conjunction with the chemical work done on heparin at the Connaught Laboratories of the University of Toronto. These experiments were reported by Murray, Jaques, Perrett and Best in 1936 and 1937.

A tendency to the formation of thrombi was created by mechanical and chemical trauma to the intima of large exposed veins, and heparin was then administered. A silk thread was placed in a vein over a distance of a few centimetres and the intima was injured by thorough external maceration with forceps. After the thread had been removed and the wound sutured, the vein was left *in situ* from 7 hours to 7 days. Obturating thrombi soon arose in animals who had received no heparin. When the blood of the animals was heparinized either locally by injections into the regional artery or else by intravenous injections, the tendency to form thrombi was found to be markedly reduced or completely inhibited. The intima was also injured in another manner by a solution of sodium ricinoleate (soricin) which was held in a peripheral vein for 3 minutes by means of stasis produced by pressure on the wall.

The blood was heparinized in slightly different ways, either before and after maceration of the vein or else afterwards only. After an initial dose of 6,000 Howell units (12 mg.) before the trauma to the vein, 2.2 units per kilo of body weight were administered per minute intravenously for 70 hours. The effect was striking as no thrombosis appeared in the treated cases. Out of 57 veins subjected to mechanical trauma in non-heparinized animals only 8 showed no thrombosis after 7 days, while 44 were occluded. In the animals treated with heparin 30 out of 37 veins revealed no thrombosis, only 7 being affected. A similar picture was presented as a result of the 70-hour heparin treatment in the animals subjected to chemical trauma (soricin) of the intima of the vein. These workers found that the effect was complete only when the animals were heparinized before injury to the vessels and if the treatment was continued for about 72 hours.

A similar experimental series was performed in 1938 by Solandt and Best, who produced coronary thrombosis in dogs by means of sodium ricinoleate. Twelve of thirteen dogs, who had been given the ricinoleate into the main trunk or a major left branch of the left coronary artery, showed myocardial degeneration, and there was demonstrable thrombosis in eleven of them. Similar lesions occurred in only one out of twelve animals if heparin was given for the 24 hours subsequent to the injury.

Further experimental support for heparin treatment was provided by Best, Cowan and MacLean in 1937. They repeated a series of experiments made by Rowntree and Shionoya in order to study the influence of heparin on the formation of thrombi in blood circulating through a collodion loop outside the body. In these experiments, later completed by Shionoya, the blood was allowed to pass from an artery to a vein through a collodion loop immersed in Ringer or glucose solution. White thrombi appeared quickly in the loop and occluded its lumen. The thrombi were formed in the ordinary manner by the agglomeration of thrombocytes, deposition of white blood corpuscles, and precipitation of fibrin. Shionoya did not succeed in preventing the formation of thrombi by heparinizing the animals. Best and his co-workers had, however, complete success in this respect. After heparinization with 1 mg. of highly active heparin per kilo of body weight, no thrombi appeared in the glass loop used by them. The authors claimed that the thrombocytes did not show the same tendency to agglutinate in the heparinized animals. In any case the blood remained fluid throughout the experiment. Shionoya had used too weak a heparin preparation, or else the dosage was not sufficient. A similar experiment, but with another end in view, had been carried out in 1928 by Haas. The blood from a patient suffering from nephritis was allowed to pass through a collodion loop lying in Ringer's solution, thus giving the urea in the blood an opportunity to dialyse out ('Blutwaschung'). Coagulation was avoided by heparinizing the patient.

The amount of heparin used in these animal experiments of Best and collaborators was generally 40—30 Toronto units (0.4— 0.3 mg.) per kg. given intravenously at hourly intervals.

Prevention of Thrombosis by Post-Operative Heparin Treatment.

The idea of using heparin to prevent the formation of thrombi was thus in the minds of all those who came into close touch with the problem. Its realization has merely depended on the availability of heparin. Consequently, the problem was at once attacked in Toronto, as well as in Stockholm, as soon as pure heparin was obtainable.

In a preliminary investigation, carried out with this treatment in view, Hedenius and Wilander established in the spring of 1935 that repeated intravenous doses of pure heparin could be administered without any inconvenience to the patients, who could be heparinized for as long as 15 hours. In doses of up to 150 mg., heparin had no influence on the general condition of the patient, on his temperature, blood-pressure, blood picture, or urine. This was what could have been expected judging from the earlier experiments of Howell (1930), Haas (1928), Mason (1924), and others. All workers state that the secondary effects disappear as the purity of the preparations increases.

In a paper written in December 1936 on heparin and vascular occlusion Murray, Jaques, Perrett and Best reported that regional heparinization had been tried on a patient in May 1935. After an operation on the brachial artery a single dose of heparin, causing a prolongation of the coagulation time from 10 to 30 minutes, had been given directly into the artery.

When once it became possible to heparinize man with the pure preparation, Clarence Crafoord, who had long been interested in this question, started in August 1935 the first systematic experimental series of this kind in Surgical Clinic II (Senior Surgeon K. H. Giertz) of Sabbatsberg Hospital, Stockholm. In the first 6 cases (submitted for publication in February, 1936) various complications appeared. It was found to be inadvisable to heparinize a patient prior to or during the operation. If the intravenous injections were given 3 hours after the operation there seemed no longer to be any danger of local haemorrhage in the operative field. The treatment was continued for the next 3 or 4 days, and consisted of either intravenous injections every fourth hour or an intravenous drip. Symptoms such as fever and chills revealed that the preparations were not fully satisfactory. In a later series of 6 cases (submitted for publication in December, 1936) no such symptoms occurred, and it was apparent that the treatment in question was quite feasible.

Crafoord's report appeared in June 1937. It was the

first such dealing with heparin treatment in man and was soon followed by other papers on the same subject.

In these experiments Crafoord observed that *heparin had considerably less effect if given during the 24 hours following an operation than when the same dose was administered pre-operatively.* The prolongation of the coagulation time, caused by a definite dose of heparin, was shorter after the operation than before. On the second or third post-operative day, the coagulation time after the same dose of heparin was the same as before the operation. The increased resistance to heparin in the early post-operative state found by Crafoord was confirmed in 1943 by de Takats, who devised a simple clinical method of measuring the heparin tolerance. 10 mg. of heparin were injected intravenously. Coagulation times were determined by the capillary tube method before injection and ten, twenty, thirty and forty minutes after it. The normal reaction to heparin was quite constant, but the coagulation time was shortened during the first few days after major operations, in thrombosis and in Buerger's disease. de Takats considered a flat tolerance curve to indicate the presence or imminence of thrombosis.

In a paper in August 1937 (submitted for publication in March of the same year) Murray, Jaques, Perrett and Best reported on both the above mentioned series of animal experiments and on a series of surgical cases treated with heparin post-operatively. The general heparinization was then maintained for as long as five days. Heparin had been administered post-operatively to 76 patients.

In the next paper, in August 1938 (submitted for publication in June of the same year) Murray and Best reported on 315 mixed cases, treated with heparin post-operatively in Toronto General Hospital. The treatment was started from 4 to 24 hours after the operation and continued for several days up to two weeks. The heparin was mainly given by intravenous drip, 10 units (0.1 mg.) in 1 ml. of saline at a rate of 25—30 drops per minute through an ordinary steel needle, which was left in the vein for periods varying from three to eight days. The coagulation time was controlled and kept fairly constant at a level of

TABLE XV

Patients Operated upon during the Period 1. 11. 1937—1. 5. 1940
Submitted to Prophylactic Post-operative Heparin Treatment
(Crafoord)

Site of operation	No. of Cases	Thrombo-embolism at autopsy	Pain in side+bloody sputum	Pain in side but no bloody sputum	Symptoms in legs (swelling, aching, tenderness)	Total certain & suspected thrombo-embolic cases	Inexplicable rise in temp. & pulse of thrombo-embolic type	No. with no sign of thrombo-embolic complications
Hernia	97	0	0	0	0	0	0	97
Gall bladder ..	85	0	0	0	0	0	2	83
Appendix	44	0	0	0	0	0	0	44
Stomach	27	0	0	0	0	0	0	27
Cancer coli & recti	11	0	0	0	0	0	0	11
Varices	19	0	0	0	0	0	0	19
Male genitals ..	20	0	0	0	0	0	1	19
Kidneys & urinary passages	13	0	0	0	0	0	0	13
Extremities	9	0	0	0	0	0	0	9
Total	325	0	0	0	0	0	3	322

15 minutes or about three times the normal value. No evidence of pulmonary embolism or thrombophlebitis was seen. For comparison the authors gave the mortality figures for thrombo-embolism at the Toronto General Hospital. After partial or complete gastrectomy they were 2.2 per cent, resection of the colon 3 per cent, resection of the rectum 6 per cent and prostatectomy 7.5 per cent. Haematomata developed in 4 of the patients given heparin post-operatively.

In 1940 the series of patients treated with heparin by Murray, MacKenzie and Wilkinson was reported by Murray to comprise 400 cases, their experience still being very favourable.

In his second publication Crafoord (1939) reported on 126 carefully controlled cases treated post-operatively with heparin, and in his next paper (Crafoord 1941, Crafoord

TABLE XVI

Patients Operated upon during the Period 1. 11. 1937—1. 5. 1940 not Submitted to Prophylactic Post-operative Heparin Treatment
(Crafoord)

Site of operation	No. of Cases	Thrombo-embolism at autopsy	Pain in side+bloody sputum	Pain in side without bloody sputum	Symptoms in the legs	Total certain thrombo-embolic cases	Inexplicable rise in temp. & pulse of thrombo-embolic type. »Uncertain»	No. with no sign of thrombo-embolic complications
Hernia	90	0	8	0	2	8	5	75
Gall bladder ..	49	1	2	4	0	3	2	40
Appendix......	74	0	7	1	0	8	4	62
Stomach	45	3	1	0	0	4	4	37
Cancer coli & recti	10	3	0	0	0	3	0	7
Varices........	13	0	0	1	2	3	0	10
Male genitals ..	11	1	0	0	1	2	0	9
Kidneys	10	1	0	0	1	2	0	8
Total	302	9	18	6	6	33	15	248

and Jorpes 1941) he reported on a total of 325 cases. Crafoord's material included only selected cases, persons over 35 years of age submitted to major operations on the gastro-intestinal tract, on the biliary system, on the urinary passages or to major operations for hernia and varices. Heparin was given four hours after the operation and continuously for an average of seven days. Usually four injections daily were given, 50+50+50+100 mg. or 75+75+75+125 mg., the amount of heparin being slowly diminished toward the end of the treatment. Even if the continuous administration of the heparin in a saline drip seemed to be more physiological, Crafoord for various reasons found it necessary to give the heparin in single intravenous injections usually 4 times a day, except in cases where a saline drip for other reasons was indicated or could easily be applied. This technique of administering heparin has since that time been generally used in Sweden.

For comparison, Crafoord collected in two series the patients of the same age submitted to similar operations in the same clinic during the period 1. 11. 1935—1. 11. 1937 before the regular heparin treatment was started, a total of 809 cases, and 273 cases operated upon but not given heparin during the period 1. 5. 1940—1. 11. 1941, when heparin was used only as an exception. In the former series there occurred 68 cases (8.4 per cent) and in the latter 21 cases (7.7 per cent) showing signs of thrombosis. During the latter period 26 patients were given heparin according to the scheme and the only evidence of thrombosis was pain in the side and bloody sputum in one of them.

The figures given for the frequency of thrombosis and pulmonary embolism among the 1,384 patients not treated with heparin were much higher than in most other statistical series. This may be explained partly by the fact that the material was selected, but mainly because even slight symptoms were carefully observed and assumed to be due to a thrombosis. A considerable number of these patients would have been ruled out if phlebographic examinations had been made. As shown by Bauer (1941) and by Hellsten (1942) the deep veins of the leg are patent in about every third case showing signs of thrombosis in the legs.

The principles of prophylactic post-operative treatment introduced by Crafoord were applied by Wetterdal (1941 a and b, 1942) in the Department of Gynaecology at the Sabbatsberg Hospital, Stockholm, in 231 *gynaecological cases*. He selected material known to give a high frequency of thrombosis: 65 operations for prolapse of the uterus, 115 operations for myoma and 51 other major laparotomies. Nine patients had previously on several occasions suffered from thrombo-embolism, *10 showed symptoms of thrombosis* 3 of them pulmonary embolism shortly before the operation; 2 were operated upon in spite of an existing thrombosis; 12 showed cardiac insufficiency; 14 had necrotic myomata and 38 were very fat. A high sedimentation rate and anaemia were very common. Fifty-two patients were between 50 and 59 years old and 25 were between 60 and 69.

In 140 cases the ordinary dose of heparin recommended

by Crafoord, $50+50+50+100$ mg. daily, was given. In one case thrombosis occurred 11 days after the heparin treatment had been concluded when the patient was still in bed because of pyelitis.

In the remainder of the series, a smaller dose of $50+50+50$ mg. was given tentatively. Two patients showed thromboembolic symptoms during the heparin treatment. In one of them pulmonary embolism appeared on the sixth day, possibly due to sepsis. She recovered, but succumbed on the 11th day to sepsis. Three other patients had symptoms of thrombosis on the third, fifth and sixth days after heparin had been withdrawn.

During the period 1. 1. 1919—31. 12. 1938, 4,766 laparotomies were performed in the Department of Gynaecology, with 192 cases of thrombo-embolism (4.03 per cent) and 24 deaths (0.5 per cent). During the period 1. 2. 1940—31. 8. 1941, a total of 563 similar operations were performed, including patients treated with heparin and the controls. 21 cases of thrombo-embolism (3.73 per cent) and 1 death occurred. Among the 231 patients treated with heparin there were 6 cases of thrombosis (2.6 per cent), if the four late cases are also included, but *there were no thromboses among the 140 cases receiving the larger dose ordinarily prescribed.* The 332 control patients showed symptoms in 15 cases or 4.5 per cent, as in the earlier period. The impression gained was that heparin, if routinely used, gives a fairly good, if not a complete protection against thrombosis.

This series also demonstrated that the protective action of heparin lasts only as long as the treatment is continued, an observation common to all clinics where heparin was in regular use. Unless the patients can move their legs or walk about freely, it is not safe to withdraw the heparin.

Prophylactic heparin treatment after childbirth was applied by Leissner at the maternity clinic at Lund. Only patients who underwent some kind of operation in connection with the delivery were selected for treatment. In 16 cases heparin was given because of thrombosis on one or several earlier occasions. The intention was to start the treatment 2 hours after delivery but in the fourth patient serious uterine bleeding occurred. From then on, the first injection was therefore given 12—24 hours after delivery. In the first series of 50 patients, 75 mg. of heparin were given every sixth hour for 2 days. In 2 cases thromboembolic symptoms appeared on the tenth and the eleventh day after delivery. In the second series of 117 patients reported in September 1941 (Leissner 1942) 50+50+50+100 mg. were given at 8, 12, 16, and 20 hours for 5 days. In this series two, possibly three, patients showed signs of late thrombosis on the fifteenth, seventeenth, and twentieth days after delivery. None of them died. In a third series of 192 similarly treated patients there were two cases of late thrombosis, both of them on the nineteenth day after delivery. They both recovered under heparin therapy. From these series it may be concluded that heparin treatment should be continued for more than 2 and even more than 5 days, particularly if the patient for some reason is compelled to stay in bed, as was the case with the four certain cases of thrombosis of Leissner. Thus, the same observation was made here as in Wetterdal's series, namely, that no protection is to be expected from the heparin treatment after its termination.

In this series, as well as in that of Wetterdal, the absence of complications during the first 10—15 days showed the beneficial effect of the heparin treatment. Complete freedom from thrombo-embolic complications during the first 10—14 days after these 309 deliveries was hardly to be expected, because in almost all of them delivery was abnormal.

In 1942 Murray and MacKenzie gave an account of 260 patients receiving heparin post-operatively. Heparin treatment was started 4 to 24 hours after operation and the patients were allowed to move about freely unaided. Among them there were 11 splenectomies. No thromboses occurred.

The *post-operative course of the 582 carefully controlled cases of Crafoord and of Wetterdal, supplemented by the 309 cases of Leissner and the 260 cases of Murray and Mac Kenzie, a total of 1151 patients, seems to prove that heparin, if routinely used over a sufficient length of time, gives an almost complete protection against thrombo-embolic com-*

plications after surgical operations and childbirth. In fact, among the 657 (325 + 140 + 192) cases receiving 250 mg. of heparin daily for 5—10 days no signs of thrombosis occurred. Only in three cases were mild complications observed two weeks after the termination of the heparin treatment. In this material, however, a high frequency of thrombosis, between 3 and 4 per cent, was expected.

The use of *doses even smaller than 250 mg. a day* reduces the frequency of thrombosis and embolism after operations. Olovson (1944) gave from the second day 100 mg. daily (50 mg. in the morning and in the evening) until the patient got up. In three years he treated 1,266 cases operated upon for intestinal or genital disorders. They were all over 30 years old. As a control he had during the same period 1,254 untreated similar cases, many of them less than 30 years old. In the first series there were 3 cases of thrombo-embolism with 2 deaths during the heparin treatment and 8 cases with 3 deaths after finishing the treatment. The complications, except in one case, followed between the 6th and 10th day after termination of the heparin treatment. Among the untreated patients thrombo-embolism occurred in 25 cases and 10 of them died. In many cases the embolic complications developed several days after the patient had got out of bed.

As an offset to these series there are others indicating that heparin has a very limited value for the prevention of thrombosis. Thus R. and G. Reimann-Hunziker (1942) made a report on 69 gynaecological cases, given heparin post-operatively in which there had been no effect from the treatment. They gave intravenously either 2×10 mg., (2×5000 Roche anticoagulant units) daily of the Roche preparation Liquemin, or 4×20 mg. for three days, a dose which is by no means sufficient. Eighteen patients were given 4 mg. each time, 1, 5, and 30 hours after operation, as recommended by Lenggenhager. Two of them developed thrombophlebitis, and a third died of pulmonary embolism. Of the whole series, nine patients showed thrombophlebitis, and three died of fulminant pulmonary embolism. This failure was due to the small amount of heparin given, one-tenth to one-fourth of the amount necessary, and to the discontinuance of the treatment after such a short time.

It is surprising that these authors used such a small dose of heparin when Rojak (1939) at the University Clinic of Bern had shown that 40—50 mg. of heparin with 500 Roche anticoagulant units per mg. must be given every fourth hour in order to obtain a sufficient degree of protection.

The University Clinic at Uppsala has had similar experience when using 4×20 mg. a day for 3—4 days in about 60 cases. In this series the incidence of thrombo-embolism was normal. Aage Nielsen at Aarhus, Denmark, in 1942 also had disappointing results after applying Crafoord's scheme post-operatively on 285 patients, for no protective action whatsoever was observed. The heparin used was a national preparation, the strength of which had not been carefully checked against the preparation used by Crafoord and Wetterdal. The two series, therefore, cannot be compared with one another. Wulff (1942) also noted no beneficial effect in 60 patients treated post-operatively with heparin according to Leng-genhager's scheme of dosage with single intravenous injections 1, 5, and 30 hours after operation, even when the heparin dose was increased to 50 mg.

Complete ignorance of the principles to be applied in the use of heparin was shown by König (1942). In a series of 120 patients, he gave doses of 100 mg. of heparin imme-diately after operation and after 8, 24, and 32 hours. As a consequence he had two fatal cases with pulmonary embolism, one pulmonary infarction and all kinds of complicating haemorrhages. He therefore recommended Sympathol and carbon dioxide inhalations in accordance with his earlier views.

The suggestion made by de Puoz (1938), that the heparin should be administered subcutaneously in the operation field, is certainly valueless, because the thrombi arise spon-taneously in the legs far from the operation field and are only to be prevented by general treatment with heparin.

Summary. The prophylactic use of heparin.

Originally this treatment was started by Crafoord to determine whether thromboses could be prevented by reduc-ing the tendency to coagulation of the blood. This question has now been answered. *The results of Crafoord and of Wetterdal and Leissner in Sweden, as well as those of Murray at the Toronto General Hospital, clearly indicate that thrombosis can be prevented by regular treatment with heparin in sufficient doses over an adequate period.*

The treatment cannot, however, be more extensively applied. The price of the drug and the repeated intravenous injections make it impractical, particularly since not more than one per cent of patients usually develop thromboses. Fortunately, we can restrict the treatment to those patients who already show signs of thrombo-embolism, because the treatment with heparin alone or in conjunction with dicumarol is sufficiently effective even then.

In spite of the drawbacks, some kind of prophylactic treatment will assuredly be resorted to in cases where the risk of thrombosis is considerable, e. g. after parturition, when a thrombosis has occurred during pregnancy, or after operations on patients who suffered from earlier repeated thrombo-embolic attacks after operations, childbirth or miscarriages. In such cases heparin has frequently been used in Swedish hospitals, starting with $50+50+50+100$ mg. (or $75+75+75+125$ mg.) of heparin a day at 8, 12, 16, and 20 hours, from the second day onward for 5—8 days, until the patient is able to get up and can move about freely. The anticoagulant therapy was combined with exercises and early ambulation. As far as is known, no failures were experienced.

After childbirth a period of 48 hours was allowed to elapse before the first injection was given. Only in vascular surgery is heparin given during or immediately after an operation.

Since thrombosis may now be controlled, operations may be safely performed on patients in whom a thrombosis is already established. In addition this control of thrombosis makes an operation or childbirth much safer for those patients who have already suffered from a pulmonary embolus or a venous thrombosis.

Disadvantages of the Tendency to Bleed during Post-Operative Heparin Treatment.

Heparinization following operations at first seemed a risky undertaking. However, if started several hours after the conclusion of the operation, it could be safely carried out. Thus, Crafoord succeeded in treating more than one hundred patients without serious complicating haemorrhages. In the long run, the tendency to bleed caused trouble as it had in all the other clinics using heparin post-operatively as a prophylactic.

In spite of careful surgical haemostasis, haemorrhages in the field of operation often give rise to haematomata. These sometimes need to be aspirated but, if not infected, they are usually harmless and do not require much attention.

Local haematomata in the wound are not as dangerous as the parenchymatous haemorrhages which give rise to sanguineous exudates in the peritoneal cavity, particularly if the latter are not detected in time. Such unexpected serious complications have occurred in four patients.

Among his 351 patients Crafoord had two in whom the heparin undoubtedly influenced the fatal outcome. In one of them an erysipelas developed from the haematoma and the outcome was fatal. In a woman of 70, a retroperitoneal haematoma developed after ileocaecotomy for cancer of the colon and she died on the third day with signs of heart failure. At autopsy 800 ml. of blood were found in the peritoneal cavity, a complication not even suspected while the patient was alive.

In another case the formation of a peritoneal haematoma was followed by symptoms of acute peritoneal irritation two days after enucleation of a myoma. The symptoms slowly increased during the day necessitating a second laparotomy and several blood transfusions which, however, led to recovery.

In his series of 231 patients Wetterdal observed moderate bleeding in the wound in four cases. In one patient a retroperitoneal haemorrhage between the bladder and the vagina necessitated an operation and a blood transfusion. Three weeks later the same patient had a similar haemorrhage in the absence of heparin. In one of his patients, aged 38, autopsy revealed 1,400 ml. of bloody exudate in the abdominal cavity. Supravaginal amputation had been performed for myoma. The day after operation her condition was poor and heparinization, with $50+50+50+100$ mg., was started on the third day. On the fourth day there was a rise in temperature and during the next five days her condition became worse. The non-protein nitrogen was high and she died of uraemia. Except for the sanguineous exudate in the peritoneal cavity no local bleeding was observed at the site of operation.

Strömbeck (1942), at the University Clinic at Lund, reports bleeding in 9 out of 40 patients, or 25 per cent of his cases. It made no difference whether the heparin treatment was started 3 or 20 to 24 hours after operation. A dose of 250 mg. of heparin was given in four injections as previously described. In two cases of cancer of the rectum there were observed infected haematomata in the wound. Out of four patients on whom pyelolithotomy was performed, three had bleeding in the field of operation and one of them died. The latter showed signs of a paralytic ileus and autopsy revealed a retroperitoneal bloody exudate.

In the carefully controlled Swedish series, comprising about 900 patients treated with heparin post-operatively, the above-mentioned complications occurred. They naturally lessen the value of post-operative prophylactic heparin treatment, even if all of them were not caused by the heparin.

Wound healing under anticoagulant therapy.

According to Butsch and Steward (1942) wound healing is not influenced by anticoagulant therapy.

Laufmann and Heller (1943) made wounds in the midline of the abdomen in a series of 80 dogs. Forty of them were then given heparin during the healing period, the coagulation time being constantly above normal, ranging from 5 to 120 minutes. At various intervals the wounds were tested for their tensile strength. The result showed a decrease on the 3rd post-operative day in the dogs treated with heparin, but otherwise there was no difference except that the heparin caused an increased incidence of haematomata. Sandblom (1944) and Bruzelius (1944) found that dicumarol administration in rabbits did not influence the healing of wounds unless the prothrombin index was very low.

9

The Administration of Heparin.

Heparin has been administered intravenously in two different ways: either continuously in saline or in single injections which are repeated several times a day.

The former method seems to be the more physiological one and has been recommended as a standard method by Murray and his co-workers.

The coagulation time of the blood is only slightly raised above the normal 5 minutes to about 15 minutes and should show a constant level (Lam 1941, 1943). This is achieved by using a solution with 20 ml. of 1 per cent strength or 200 mg. (20,000 Toronto units) of heparin per litre and giving 15—25 drops per minute. Slightly more than 1,000 units (10 mg.) are given per hour and about 1,200 ml. of saline daily.

The continuous method cannot be applied when the patient is out of bed, nor in the presence of renal or cardiac disorders, because of the volume of liquid administered.

In Sweden, heparin has been given almost exclusively in single injections. In routine work, the continuous method proved to have so many disadvantages that single injections were tentatively tried by Crafoord. The results seemed to be good and this technique was therefore adopted and further elaborated. It was found advantageous to use a concentrated 5 per cent solution of the sodium salt of heparin, so that only 1—3 ml. were to be injected at a time. A very fine needle was recommended for the injections to avoid spoiling the veins.

This simplified technique was a great help in introducing heparin therapy. The administration of single large doses of heparin, giving a fluctuating concentration in the blood might seem uneconomical. However, the results reported from the Swedish clinics, obtained with a technique usually including four intravenous injections during the day, are quite comparable with those obtained by the continuous technique and the total amount of heparin used is about the same. Only in exceptional cases have injections been made every four or six hours during the night.

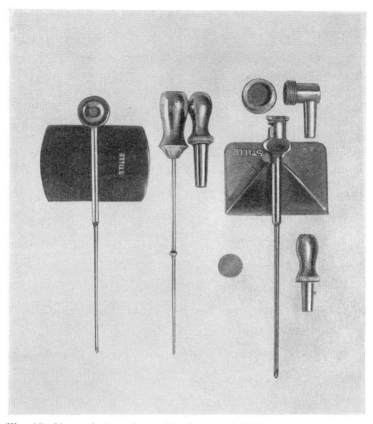

Fig. 15. Olovson's heparin needle (left) and Edlund's needle (right)
with detachable parts. Between them a flexible silver cannula.

This technique of repeated injections is much improved
by inserting a needle which is left *in situ* for a number of
days (Murray 1940 a, Olovson 1940, Hellsten 1942, p. 83).
Olovson made a special needle for this purpose. The detachable metal cap which contains a rubber membrane is un-
screwed, and the needle inserted in the vein. The cap is
then replaced, and subsequent injections of heparin are
made through the rubber membrane with a fine needle.
This allows injections to be given by less skilled attendants

and, if necessary, during the night when the patient is asleep.

A similar needle has been described by Edlund (1946). A flexible silver cannula which is inserted surgically into a vein may sometimes, e. g. in infants, prove to be of value. A technique for the injection through a rubber tube has been suggested by Kolff (1942).

Walker (1945) suggested an intramuscular administration of heparin, four injections spaced over a 24-hour period. A more controllable effect should thereby be obtained than by giving the heparin intravenously. The subcutaneous route was very painful and gave rise to local reactions.

Lindgren and Walldén (1944), using the ordinary equipment for intramedullar infusion, administered heparin intrasternally. They claimed that the effect of heparin on the coagulation time of the blood is the same as when heparin is given intravenously. The needle is left *in situ* for several days and injections can be given day and night. This technique may prove to be of value for a continuous drip when the veins are unsuitable. It is especially useful for infants and young babies where the tibia or some other fairly thick long bone is chosen.

Heparin has also been administered intramuscularly after procaine anaesthesia in a 7, 10 or 14 per cent mixture of beeswax in sesame oil (Bryson and Code 1944). The same method had previously been applied for the administration of desoxicorticosterone and histamine.

To obtain a slow and more even absorption of the heparin Loewe and Rosenblatt (1944) mixed it with a menstruum containing 15—30 per cent of gelatine, 5—12 per cent of glucose, 1—1.5 per cent of acetic acid and water. Adrenalin, ephedrine and eucupine were added and different formulae were worked out. The menstruum liquified at 27° C and the handling of it under sterile conditions was a rather difficult procedure. A prolonged action of the heparin, lasting for 3—5 days, was claimed to be obtained on intramuscular or preferably subcutaneous administration of the menstruum. 100—300 mg. of heparin in 2—4 ml. of the menstruum were deposited at a time.

Heparin as a Therapeutic Agent in Thrombo-Embolism.

While it was quite commonly accepted, as is evident from the previous quotations, that heparin ought to be an ideal prophylactic for thrombosis, nobody imagined that it would become still more useful as a therapeutic agent in thrombosis. Once a coagulum was formed, it seemed unlikely that heparin would exert any influence upon the thrombus except for the prevention of its further growth. Thus Ochsner, in 1939, considered that heparin would have a limited use in cases of thrombophlebitis and phlebothrombosis. The experience gained in the meantime has shown, however, that the thrombus, under regular heparin treatment, is not only checked in its growth, but also that all the acute symptoms recede. By a comparatively recent experiment, Rabinowitch and Pines (1943) demonstrated that a venous thrombosis can be made to disappear under the influence of heparin. They induced thrombosis of the jugular veins in rabbits by grasping the exposed vein between the fingers and pulling it forcibly so as to injure the endothelial lining. A clot formed more promptly if the flow of blood was subsequently slowed up by partial constriction of the vein by tying a loose ligature around it. On re-opening the wound to examine the vein it was found without exception to be thrombosed. It remained patent, however, if heparin had been given shortly before the trauma or if 10 mg. of heparin were injected intravenously twice daily for 2—5 days, beginning from the first day. Even the endothelium regenerated. If similar treatment with heparin was started on the second day after the trauma, when a thrombus already occluded the vessel, the thrombus was found to have

disappeared at the end of the treatment in four out of
five rabbits. If heparin was given on the third day after
the trauma the thrombus disappeared in three out of six
cases. Heparin given on the sixth day did not influence
the thrombus.

Apparently, the heparin facilitates the enzymic fibrin-
olysis of fresh clots. Even if the heparin injections were
begun on the third day, they retarded the thrombosis. These
findings have a very important bearing on the treatment
of early thrombosis with heparin. First, they show that the
blood can dissolve a loose, fresh clot if the coagulation
mechanism is put out of action, and secondly they prove
that intermittent injections twice daily can replace to a
certain extent the continuous intravenous infusions.

Much could be written about the theoretical grounds for
heparin treatment. It would not serve any useful purpose
however. The deciding point will always be, how heparin
in practice influences the course of the thrombo-embolic
disease.

In Sweden, this question was raised in an unusual way.
In the spring of 1937 Crafoord published the first report
on prophylactic heparin treatment in man, and Holmgren,
Wilander and Jorpes discovered that heparin is produced
by the mast cells. A lively interest in this question followed.

As a result, a physician in Stockholm, Holmin, later in the
year tried the new remedy in a case of fresh acute thrombosis in the central retinal vein in a young person. Well
aware of the hopeless prognosis, he gave a tentative dose
of 150 mg. of pure heparin intravenously three to four
times daily over a period of 10 days beginning on the third
day of the illness.

Ploman describes the course of this case as quite unusual,
for the patient regained a visual acuity of 0.9 in 9 days.
The haemorrhages in the eye grounds were reabsorbed with
uncommon rapidity. In a second case, described by Boström and William-Olsson, where the lesion was 1 month
old, visual acuity rose from 0.1 to 0.4 in 5 days and later
to 0.6 during treatment with 100—150 mg. heparin two to
three times daily. The unusual course of these two conse-

cutive cases made these ophthalmologists inclined to ascribe
the result to the treatment with heparin.

The further development in this particular field will be
dealt with in a separate chapter.

In the same year Magnusson (1938 c) used heparin successfully in a case of thrombosis of the posterior inferior
cerebellar artery (Wallenberg's syndrome).

In their paper of August 1938, Murray and Best reported
28 cases of spontaneous thrombophlebitis and 7 cases of
pulmonary embolism treated with heparin. All the cases of
embolism showed rapid clinical improvement within 24
hours and had less pain in the leg and chest. Although
several of the cases had serious recurring embolisms every
few days before the intravenous injection of heparin was
started, no further embolism, with one possible but no
proven exception, occurred after the treatment was started.
The 28 cases of spontaneous thrombophlebitis, treated with
heparin, showed no evidence of embolism, and the clinical
signs and symptoms, pain, swelling, tenderness and fever,
appeared to show more rapid improvement than in a control
group.

In his second paper, Crafoord (1939) stated that he had
given heparin to 20 cases with manifest thrombo-embolic
complications. In some of these, both the general and local
symptoms receded strikingly rapidly. There were in particular 5 cases described in detail in which the recovery
proceeded very rapidly. In most of the cases, however, the
disease showed a normal course.

In 1939, Magnusson (1940) administered heparin to a
woman with severe pulmonary embolism and thrombosis in
both legs, complicating a post-partum scarlatina. The temperature became normal in a few days and the patient, who
had been ill for 6 weeks and was very emaciated, recovered.
(Fig. 16.)

In his Hunterian Lecture, given at the Royal College of
Surgeons, London, in June 1939, Murray (1940 a) reported
400 cases treated post-operatively with heparin without any
thromboses developing, 50 cases of thrombophlebitis treated
under carefully controlled conditions, and 22 cases of pul-

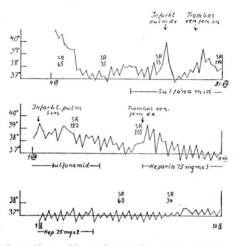

Fig. 16. The immediate effect of heparin on the body temperature in a patient who during the course of one month had two pulmonary infarctions and thrombosis in both legs.

monary embolism. Most of the patients were quite ill, with high fever and oedema of the legs. He gave the most favourable opinion about the treatment. The average case of acute thrombophlebitis had been treated with heparin for about ten days. The effect of heparin was most noticeable when a case was seen very early in the development of the disease. After the first three or four days, the patient was asked to move about actively in bed, and after about two further days active exercises in preparation for getting the patient out of bed were insisted upon. The time in bed averaged 10—12 days. He described the effect of heparin as very striking in the 22 cases of pulmonary embolism. None of them died and no massive embolism occurred during the treatment, although most of these cases were of a serious nature. Within a few hours there was a marked clinical improvement, and within 24 hours all the patients stated frankly that they were improved.

His experience in the use of heparin for these purposes, as well as in vascular surgery, e. g. embolectomies and arterial resections, and in mesenteric thrombosis, were given by Murray in two papers of about the same date (1940 b and c) and in a paper in 1941.

Experience in Sweden with heparin treatment in acute thrombosis and in pulmonary embolism, was presented at a symposium on heparin and thrombosis, held at the joint meeting of the Swedish Society of Surgeons and the Swedish Society for Internal Medicine, December 1940 (Jorpes, Crafoord, Wetterdal, Leissner, Clason, Bauer, Hedenius 1941).

Clason reported three cases of very severe pulmonary embolism, treated successfully with heparin. Crafoord summarized his results as follows: "Our material, which comprised not more than about 40 cases, was heterogenous. In many instances, considerable subjective relief was experienced even after a few heparin injections. We have also noted that the temperature and pulse rate often returned to normal in a surprisingly short time. In other patients, who showed marked swelling of one or both legs, increasing rapidly in conjunction with high fever, the swelling had almost disappeared within a few days, and the temperature had fallen. But on the other hand, in other similar cases, the heparin had no demonstrable effect. The course of the disease in these patients was about the same as it would have been without heparin."

A similar opinion was given by Wetterdal, who had treated 20 cases: "Six of these patients had pulmonary embolism. They all got well. It seems as if the course of the disease was considerably shortened by the heparinization. During the treatment any swelling present rapidly decreased, the pain disappeared, and the temperature fell to normal within 3 to 5 days. Discerning patients suffering from pulmonary embolism stated that they felt immediate relief after the injections. The anguish and uneasiness lessened, the cyanosis diminished and the dyspnoea was relieved."

Murray (1940 b) reported 72 cases of thrombophlebitis, among them 26 cases with pulmonary embolism treated with heparin. "The improvement in the clinical course was impressive. The pain, temperature and oedema subsided much more rapidly than in a control group of cases. After one week's treatment they were out of bed exercising actively and able to be discharged from the hospital.

In 1942 Murray and MacKenzie reported on 218 cases of acute thrombophlebitis treated with heparin. In 63 of them pulmonary embolism occurred prior to the treatment. There was no further pulmonary embolism and a striking subjective and objective improvement. None of the patients died. The specific effect of heparin on thrombosis was considered as evidence in favour of the non-infective theory of the cause of thrombophlebitis.

The amount of heparin administered was regulated according to the individual need of the patient. *1,000—1,800 Toronto units were given hourly in an intravenous drip, or the same amount as used by the Swedish authors*, 280—500 mg. a day of the Swedish standard heparin with 80 Toronto units per mg.

A very favourable opinion of the effect of heparin in preventing new attacks of embolism in early cases was given by Priestly, Essex and Barker at the Mayo Clinic in 1941. The administration of heparin during the initial embolic stage was often accompanied by more prompt improvement of clinical symptoms of the embolism than might have been otherwise expected. Their impression of the treatment in thrombophlebitis was that the course of the disease was shortened when heparin was given promptly following recognition of the condition. They had given heparin to 55 patients. Transient haematuria was observed in a few instances.

A dramatic therapeutic effect of heparin treatment has been reported by several authors. Thus Boland and Roney (1941) published a case of extensive generalized thrombophlebitis following eclampsia and Cesarean section, in which during the course of six weeks thrombosis developed in the external jugular veins, both axillary veins, both femoral veins and elsewhere, making a total of eleven different sites. At first, an inactive heparin preparation was tried but it had no influence on the coagulation time of the blood nor on the patient's condition. When the Toronto heparin was administered the clotting time rose rapidly and the patient showed a dramatic general improvement within 24 hours. The inflammatory process in the neck and the arm subsided rapidly and the temperature returned to normal in 5 days. There were no further thrombi and the patient recovered.

The Work of Bauer at the Mariestad Hospital, Sweden.

The most valuable contribution to the development of this question has been made by Gunnar Bauer. Originally interested in the study of the venous system in the legs before and after spontaneous thrombosis (Bauer 1940), he very soon found that incipient initial thrombosis in the legs, as shown by phlebographic X-ray examinations, was checked by heparin treatment. The routine use of heparin aborted an early thrombosis. The acute symptoms, the pyrexia, swelling, tenderness and pain in the legs disappeared in a surprisingly short time. In his first report in December 1940 (Bauer 1941 a and b), he summarized his preliminary results as follows: "21 cases, where the diagnosis of early thrombosis in the lower leg had been confirmed by means of venography, were treated with heparin, 3×100 mg. daily for 3—5 days. All of them quickly became free of symptoms and got up in a few days. Of 32 similar cases not treated with heparin, 2 died, 3 showed pulmonary embolism, 8 pulmonary infarction and 24 spread of the thrombosis to the femoral veins. Average length of time in bed, 43 days."

In September 1941 (Bauer 1942 b) he reported 51 cases treated in the same way. No tendency toward bleeding or other disadvantages were observed. None of them died. They were out of bed after 6—7 days.

Besides the early heparin treatment Bauer paid special attention to free active movements, undoubtedly a detail of vital importance. Movements of the legs were started almost immediately, and as soon as the acute symptoms disappeared, the patient was allowed to sit in a chair or to get up.

This series of Bauer at Mariestad was supplemented by a series of 89 cases treated by Hellsten (1942), who applied

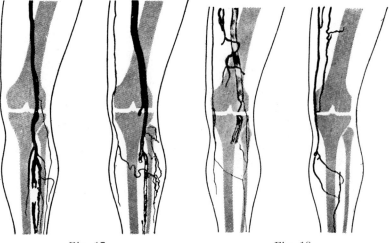

Fig. 17.   Fig. 18

Fig. 17. Phlebographic picture of an initial (left) and a more advanced
(right) thrombosis of the veins of the calf (G. Bauer).

Fig. 18. Left, a waving fresh thrombus not filling the lumen of
vena femoralis; right, complete thrombosis of the deep veins in the
leg with only superficial venous return (G. Bauer).

on a larger scale the same principle of early diagnosis by
means of phlebography and early adequate heparin treatment in some of the Stockholm hospitals. He had also under
his care more advanced cases with thrombosis spreading to
the femoral vein and with pulmonary embolism. He divided
his material into three groups, A, B, and C. His results
were as follows:

Group A. 55 cases of phlebographically certain thrombosis in the calf of the leg, 10 of them with
pulmonary embolism. Pyrexia lasting 8.3 days.
Got up on an average 7.6 days after detection
of the symptoms of thrombosis.

Group B. 25 patients with thrombosis in the thigh and
phlegmasia alba dolens with or without embolism. Pyrexia lasting 8.7 days. Got up after
8.5 days.

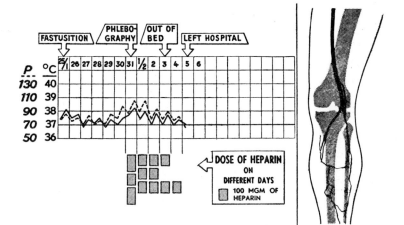

Fig. 19. Typical case of thrombosis of the veins of the calf treated
with heparin.

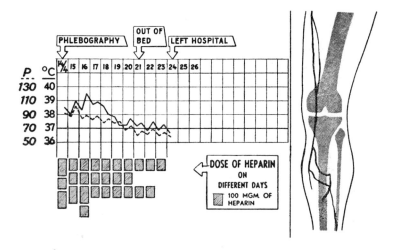

Fig. 20. A case of phlegmasia alba dolens treated with heparin.

Group C. 9 cases of pulmonary embolism with no certain
signs of thrombosis in the legs. Pyrexia lasting
8.7 days. Got up after 8.1 days.

Besides these 89 cases with phlebographically verified thrombosis or pulmonary embolism, Hellsten obtained a negative phlebographic picture in 46 other patients showing more or less typical clinical symptoms. Thus in every third case, where a thrombosis in the leg was suspected, the deep veins of the calf remained patent. The same finding had been made earlier by Bauer in his material. The diagnosis becomes certain after ruling out these cases. All cases with acute phlebitic symptoms in the superficial veins alone were also ruled out in this material. Such patients were treated with cold wet compresses only and were allowed to walk freely.

Among the 149 patients of Bauer and Hellsten the only death was in a case of phlegmasia alba dolens in which the treatment could not be begun until a week after the appearance of the symptoms.

These results seemed astonishingly good. Irrespective of whether the thrombus was restricted to the lower leg or had involved the femoral vein, or whether a pulmonary embolism had occurred, the patients responded in the same way to the heparin treatment. The pyrexia subsided and diminution of the swelling and pain in the leg followed within 2 to 4 days. Generally the patients themselves testified to the difference in the symptoms. They were soon able to move their legs and as soon as the temperature became normal, or even before that, they were allowed to get up.

The beneficial effect of heparin treatment was most clearly reflected by the fall in temperature setting in on the 2nd to 4th day of the treatment. *If no reaction of this kind follows, the pyrexia is probably due to other causes.*

In a series of 420 obstetrical cases with thrombo-embolism, not treated with heparin, Hellsten found pyrexia, probably due to thrombosis, lasting on an average for 23.6 days per patient. Among 21 cases treated with heparin from the same clinic the corresponding figure was 9.5 days.

Hellsten describes the method of treatment as suggested by Bauer as follows:

"After the diagnosis had been made — usually with the aid of phlebography — treatment was begun immediately.

The heparin was administered intravenously every 4 hours during the day. There was generally time for one or two injections on the first day. Four daily doses were given, the first at 8 a. m. and the following doses at noon, 4 p. m., and 8 p. m. The first and the last dose were generally between 100 and 150 mg., occasionally 200 mg. The two intervening doses during the day were usually from 50 to 100 mg.; in a few instances they were raised to 150 mg. The dosage was modified to some extent according to the weight of the patient. In case of pulmonary embolism, the customary treatment with eupaverine, administered intravenously, was employed simultaneously with heparin in large doses.

When the local symptoms of thrombosis had receded, and the temperature and pulse had returned to normal, the heparin injections were reduced to three per day, 100—125 mg. + 50—75 mg. + 100—125 mg., the most suitable times being 8 a. m., 2 p. m. and 8 p. m. The patient was allowed to sit in a chair. Before sitting up, the leg was wrapped in an elastic bandage from the great toe to the knee. If no reaction such as a rise in temperature or intensified discomfort in the legs occurred, the patient was allowed to put weight on the leg on the following day by walking for a short time in the room. An elastic bandage was always used when the patient got up and walked about. On the day the patient was allowed to get up, heparin was administered in 2 doses, 100—125 mg. at 8 a. m., and at 8 p. m. The following day, the distance walked was increased, and the patient was allowed to remain up until he got tired. As a rule only one morning dose of 100—125 mg. was then given. It was sometimes possible at this stage to discontinue the heparin treatment completely; with other patients it was necessary to allow three or four more days to elapse.

On discharge the patient was instructed to continue wearing the elastic bandage as long as there was a feeling of tenseness and swelling in the leg. Tenseness and slight swelling of the ankle was often present during the first week the patient was up, but these symptoms disappeared fairly rapidly. The last to disappear was the swelling. The instructions were to keep the bandage on all day. During the first month out of hospital the leg was to be rested now and then during the day by the patient lying down and elevating it. After two or three weeks more the bandage could be discarded.''

During the five years since October 1940, Bauer has consistently applied the above mentioned principles, namely, early diagnosis, if necessary by means of phlebography, immediate heparin treatment with large doses, free active movements and early ambulation. Every case of deep venous thrombosis and of pulmonary embolism has been treated in the same way. His results are summarized in table XVII.

TABLE XVII

Heparin Treatment of Thrombosis and Pulmonary Embolism at the Mariestad Hospital, Mariestad, Sweden, 1940—1945.

	1929—1938 Conservative treatment	$^1/_{10}$ 1940—$^{30}/_9$ 1945 Heparin treatment
Number of patients . . .	25,628	16,495
Number of cases of thrombosis	264	209
Fatal pulmonary embolism	47	3
Mortality among the cases of thrombosis	18 %	1.4 %
Average stay in bed . . .	40 days	4.7 days
Sequelae	Serious	None; or very slight

As is evident from the table, the *mortality* has dropped to one-tenth of its original figure. In fact, after more than 7,500 operations during the five years, there have been no deaths from thrombosis. In one case a superficial thrombosis suddenly went to the deeper veins and caused a fatal pulmonary embolism before any treatment was considered. The other two fatal cases had for various reasons received an insufficient or practically no heparin treatment. In this way the frequency of fatal pulmonary embolism was reduced from 4—5 per annum to one per two years.

The average *stay in bed* due to thrombosis was also shortened to about one-tenth of the previous figure i. e. about five days. The incidence of the *sequelae of thrombosis* is of greatest interest. As will be seen from table XXIII on page 158 the thrombus remained in the lower leg in 80 per cent of the cases, the discomfort of the swelling of the legs, induration and ulcers thus being avoided. Among the 209 cases, however, 79 were admitted to the Mariestad Hospital because of thrombosis which had developed in their homes or at other hospitals. They are consequently to be regarded as late cases in which the beneficial influence of the early heparin treatment was not to be fully expected. An even better final result thus might have been obtained.

The Results of the First Five Years' Treatment with Heparin in Some Swedish Clinics.

The principle of treating early thrombosis with heparin, active movements and early ambulation was soon applied in many clinics in Sweden. In 1942, administration of dicumarol either alone or in conjunction with heparin was introduced. Since that time the use of anticoagulants in the treatment of thrombosis and pulmonary embolism has been widely applied.

After the introduction of anticoagulant therapy in various clinics a remarkable change took place in the course of these cases.

At a medical clinic in Stockholm, 9 out of 16 patients with thrombosis died during 1940 and 1941. In 1942 heparin therapy was more or less consistently applied, and in 1943—1944 heparin and dicumarol were given. In these years 22 cases of deep venous thrombosis occurred, without any deaths. In 1944, Linde found at one surgical clinic 17 deaths among 71 patients with thrombosis, and at another 5 deaths among 41 cases. At the last mentioned clinic 26 cases had received specific treatment; among these there were no fatalities. During the same period, Crafoord and Wetterdal, at the Sabbatsberg Hospital, treated 74 cases of deep venous thrombosis or embolism with no deaths. At the surgical unit of the Jönköping Hospital, Feltström found that 11 out of 33 untreated patients died during the years 1940—43, as compared with only one of the 31 cases treated with anticoagulants during 1942—1944. *There was thus one death among 153 treated cases and there were 42 deaths among 161 untreated cases. It appears probable that many of the deaths in the untreated group could have been prevented by specific treatment.*

In contrast to the good results obtained by specific therapy a study of the case histories at the different clinics revealed in some of them an unbelievable carelessness in the treatment of the patients. The fatal outcome and the prolonged stay in hospital seemed to be expected. The histories of some of these cases are given here.

Case 1. A young primipara. During her pregnancy she had deep thrombosis of the leg, *which was treated by confinement to bed for two months.* Parturition normal. When she got up she died of pulmonary embolism.

Error in treatment: The patient's thrombosis during pregnancy ought to have been treated with heparin, and from the second or third day after delivery, she ought to have received 250—300 mg. of heparin a day and to have been told to move about in bed until she got up. In all probability there would then have been no fatal disaster.

Case 2. A married woman aged 30. Sept. 7, normal delivery. Sept. 17, tenderness in right calf. Thrombosis? Kept immobilized. Sept. 19, bilateral thrombosis. Sept. 22, a sharp pain in side, but she was not greatly affected. Sept. 30, left leg greatly swollen. Oct. 5, a severe attack of dyspnoea due to embolism. Oct. 7, death.

Case 3. A woman aged 36, who was admitted on Feb. 21 with a diagnosis of cholecystitis. Operation Feb. 23, cholecystectomy and drainage. March 3, sharp pain in left side of chest, fever, and cyanosis. High fever from March 3 onwards. Legs normal. March 8, acute embolism and death.

Case 4. A man aged 20, diagnosed as a case of ulcerative colitis. Since Aug. 15, 1942, he had had an aching pain in his left leg, which had been slightly swollen. Admitted Aug. 20. Left ankle and calf slightly swollen. Tenderness on palpation over the calf.

Temp. 38.2° C (101° F). Aug. 23, aching pain and tenderness in right calf. Aug. 28, sudden collapse, with severe pains in chest and dyspnoea. Death within half an hour. P. A. D.: pulmonary embolism. A thrombus was found firmly attached to the wall of the vena iliaca communis.

Thus, the development of a new thrombosis in the other leg, arising in the sole of the foot and extending upwards, was witnessed at the hospital without anything being done about it.

Case 5. A 55 year old man who had always had good health. Sept. 5, a bad fainting attack. An aching pain in the chest. Cardiac infarction was suspected. Admitted the same day. Temp. 38° C (100.5° F). No cyanosis. Pulse 68. Blood pressure 165/90. Nothing abnormal found in the lungs. Sept. 16, another attack of pain in chest. Temp. 39.2° C (102.5° F). Sept. 17, a slight cough. Blood-streaked sputum. Sept. 20, no symptoms. Sept. 23, a sharp pain in left side of chest. Bloody sputum, cyanosis, pulse scarcely discernible. Death at 6 p. m.

The absence of cyanosis and the normal pulse and blood pressure exclude the possibility of a coronary infarction. The bloody sputum made the diagnosis of pulmonary infarction certain.

Case 6. A woman aged 75, who was operated on for cataract on Aug. 22, 1941. Aug. 30, symptoms of embolism from the chest, pyrexia; sulphapyridine administered. Sept. 2, admitted to the hospital suffering from signs of infarction of the lung. Oct. 9, rise in temperature. Sulphathiazole-resistant. Oct. 11, thrombosis in right leg. Oct. 13, sudden death from "Collapse of the peripheral circulation". P. A. D.: Emboli obstructing the pulmonary artery and attached to the walls, greyish red and red thrombi in the veins of the pelvis and thigh.

It should be noted here that the "pneumonia" was resistant to sulphonamides and that signs of thrombosis in the leg appeared two days before a freshly formed embolus originating from this caused the patient's death. In this case the age would not have constituted any obstacle to a successful treatment.

Case 7. An unmarried woman aged 21. Under treatment for gonococcal arthritis of the right hip. Jan. 16, 1941, had suffered for a few days from an aching pain and swelling in the hip and thigh. Temp. 39—40° C (102—3° F). Thrombosis of the femoral vein diagnosed. Jan. 26, sudden death from pulmonary embolism.

Case 8. A 46 year old woman was sent from an eye clinic with a diagnosis of glaucoma, pneumonia, and thrombosis. Feb. 11, signs of thrombosis in left popliteal vein. Slight tenderness on palpation. Feb. 14, no local symptoms. Thrombosis not definitely established. Feb. 25, an attack of palpitation. Pulse 140. No reaction to digitalis. Feb. 26, left leg very swollen and oedematous. Thrombosis of the femoral vein diagnosed. March 26, leg still swollen. March 29, leg even more swollen and tense. The day before she had had a sudden attack, with palor and cold sweats. Pulse soft. Embolism? April 14, the patient was allowed to start moving her leg. April 20, the patient can now walk about, though with difficulty. *Course, 9 weeks.* When re-examined 4 years later her leg was found to be badly swollen and indurated.

Case 9. A man aged 47, who was operated upon on May 28, 1940 for inguinal hernia. June 2, a sharp pain in right side. June 12, pyrexia. Pain in left side. X-ray of lungs: pneumonia or infarction. Admitted June 14, with moderately severe cyanosis. Pains in chest. Temp. 39° C. Temp. 38° C (100.5° F) until July 9. Temperature not normal until July 24. June 20, a fresh attack of pain in chest. June 23, an aching pain in left leg and back of knee. Leg much swollen. June 26, left leg displayed the typical picture of thrombosis. July 29, sat in a chair. Discharged Aug. 16. *Hospital stay due to thrombosis, 10 weeks.*

There is no reason to expect that any of these seven cases would of necessity have ended fatally. With an appropriate treatment all of them could probably have been saved. The last two cases ought to have stayed in bed for about a week or ten days instead of 10 weeks.

The contribution of Zilliacus.

In 1945, Zilliacus analyzed the effect of the introduction of the new principles of treatment as expressed in the mortality of thrombo-embolism, confinement to bed, and disabling sequelae of deep venous thrombosis in the legs. He studied the case reports of 1,158 cases of thrombosis among 256,282 patients from 19 Swedish clinics during the period 1940—1944. In this material every fourth case did not receive any specific treatment, while the remaining cases were regularly treated with anticoagulants. Zilliacus paid particular attention to the sequelae of thrombosis and therefore made a follow-up examination on all the patients previously treated for thrombo-embolism who could be traced. The way in which the material was divided into different groups, the frequency of complicating emboli and of fatal pulmonary embolism may be seen in table XVIII.

The frequency of thrombosis, 0.51—0.37 per cent, is low in all the series as compared with the figures given in tables 26 and 27. This is partly due to the fact that only cases with an evident deep venous thrombosis or pulmonary embolism were considered, and partly also to the active movement therapy and early ambulation, which to a large extent were applied in the different clinics. It is evident from the table that in 85 per cent of the fatal cases (in 135 cases out of 161) death was caused by an occult thrombosis which was not observed before the sudden fatal pulmonary embolism occurred. In these cases no specific treatment

TABLE XVIII

The Frequency of Thrombosis and Embolism after Surgical Operations, Gynaecological Operations, Childbirth, and in Medical Cases (Zilliacus, 19 Swedish Clinics, 1940—1945)

Cases	Thrombo-embolic cases		Pulmonary embolism			Fatal pulmonary embolism				No. of follow-up examinations
	No.	Percentage of total cases	No.	Percentage of		No.	Percentage of			
				Thrombotic cases	Total cases		Thrombo-embolic cases	Embolic cases	Total cases	
Surgical 125,524	646	0.51	284	43.0	0.22	132	20.2	46.1	0.103	387
Obstetric-gynaecological 96,672	387	0.40	85	21.9	0.08	11	2.8	12.9	0.011	318
Medical...... 34,086	125	0.37	39	31.2	0.114	18	15.2	48.6	0.056	60
Totals...... 256,282	1158		408			161[1]				765

[1] Out of the 161 cases of fatal pulmonary embolism, 135 occurred without other signs of thrombosis, and 26 after previous signs of thrombosis.

could therefore be applied. The very low mortality rates, 0.103, 0.011 and 0.056 per cent in the surgical, gynaecological and medical series, could thus have been still lower if more attention had been paid to early diagnosis.

The proportion between the number of cases with thrombosis in the lower leg only and the number of cases with thrombosis of the thigh.

Among 214 conservatively treated cases the above mentioned proportion is as one to four. If the corresponding figure for the specifically treated cases is examined, it will be found that in half of the cases the thrombosis remains localized in the lower leg.

TABLE XIX

Stay in Bed and Rise in Temperature in 790 Cases of Deep Venous Thrombosis given no Specific Treatment, or Treated with Heparin, with Heparin and Dicumarol, or with Dicumarol Alone
(*Zilliacus 1946*)

Treatment	Site	No. of cases of thrombosis (excluding sudden pulmonary embolism alone)	Time from appearance of symptoms of thrombosis to patient getting up Days (mean)	Duration of fever after appearance of signs of thrombosis. Days (mean)
No specific treatment	Calf	43 ⎫	35.1	21.0
	Thigh, or calf and thigh	171 ⎬ 214		
Heparin	Calf	155 ⎱	8.7	6.9
	Thigh, or calf and thigh	187	11.1	8.7
Heparin and dicumarol	Calf	40 ⎰ 576	8.3	7.3
	Thigh, or calf and thigh	63	10.5	7.6
Dicumarol	Calf	71	8.2	7.5
	Thigh, or calf and thigh	60 ⎭	11.3	8.8
	Total	790		

TABLE XX

Pulmonary Embolism, and Spread to the Second Leg, in 790 Cases of Deep Venous Thrombosis given no Specific Treatment, or Treated with Heparin, with Heparin and Dicumarol, or with Dicumarol Alone (Zilliacus 1946)

Treatment	Site	No. of cases of thrombosis (excluding sudden pulmonary embolism alone)	No. of cases of pulmonary embolism complicating thrombosis				Cases in which thrombosis spread to the other leg
			During active thrombosis	Before active thrombosis	After active thrombosis	Fatal cases	
No specific treatment	Calf	43 ⎱214 171	60	8	5	20	66
	Thigh, or calf and thigh						
Heparin	Calf	155	2 (+1 before treatment began)	5	4	2	2 (+1 recurrence in same leg)
	Thigh, or calf and thigh	187	4 (+3 before treatment began)	7	1	..	3 (+4 after treatment +1 recurrence in same leg)
Heparin and Dicumarol	Calf	40 ⎱576	..	1	..	..	1 after treatment
	Thigh, or calf and thigh	63	(3 before treatment began)	4	..	..	2
Dicumarol	Calf	71	(1 before treatment began)	2	..	..	1
	Thigh, or calf and thigh	60	2 (+2 before treatment began)	..	..	1	..
Total		790				23	

The importance of this is evident from the follow-up examination of the sequelae in the lower extremity which will be dealt with in a separate chapter.

Recumbency and fever. (Table XIX.)

The time the patient stays in bed because of the thrombosis is three to four times shorter among the patients receiving specific therapy. This is, however, not only due to the specific therapy. In the conservative treatment confinement to bed is a form of therapy and the time the patient is in bed could certainly have been shortened in many cases. The speedy disappearance of the symptoms of acute thrombosis such as pain, swelling and fever as a result of the specific treatment allows early ambulation, which is impossible in the conservatively treated cases.

The duration of pyrexia is a more indisputable expression of the course of the disease. Among the conservatively treated cases the mean duration of pyrexia was 21 days. Those cases receiving specific therapy were pyrexial for a period of about 7 days. Heparin showed the greatest activity in reducing the temperature.

Spread of the thrombosis to the other leg. (Table XX.)

Among the 214 conservatively treated cases the thrombosis spread to the other leg in 66 cases (31 per cent). Among 576 cases receiving specific therapy there were 9 such cases (1.6 per cent). In almost all cases specifically treated the spread of thrombosis to the other leg was prevented. On the other hand it took place in nearly one out of three conservatively treated cases. In the follow-up examination of these patients the sequelae, if present, were bilateral in practically every case.

Pulmonary embolism in cases with clinical symptoms of thrombosis. (Table XX.)

Among the 214 conservatively treated cases 59 were complicated by pulmonary embolism (28 per cent). Among 576 cases receiving specific therapy there were 8 cases of pulmonary embolism (1.4 per cent).

If those cases of pulmonary embolism are included which occurred subsequent to the treatment and after the patient was allowed up, then the percentages will be 31 for those conservatively treated and 2.1 for those receiving specific therapy.

In 20 cases out of 214 (9.4 per cent) of the conservatively treated cases with thrombosis in the leg, the patient died from pulmonary embolism.

Among the 576 cases receiving specific therapy, there were only three fatalities (0.5 per cent), two of them after the termination of the treatment.

The effect of the specific therapy in thrombosis is evident from the frequency of pulmonary embolism which occurred fifteen times more often among the conservatively treated cases than among the patients receiving specific therapy, and from the fact that while nine out of every hundred conservatively treated patients died from pulmonary embolism, only one in two hundred died among the specifically treated cases.

Cases of pulmonary embolism without other clinical symptoms of thrombosis in the material examined by Zilliacus (Table XXI).

There were 282 cases of sudden pulmonary embolism without other signs of thrombosis. In 114 cases death followed either immediately or in a very short time.

TABLE XXI

The Influence of the Treatment on the Course of Pulmonary Embolism Occurring without Other Signs of Thrombosis.
(Zilliacus 1946.)

	Number	Deaths
Sudden death	114	114
Conservatively treated cases .	65	21 (30 %)
Cases treated with heparin or heparin + dicumarol . . .	103	0
	282	

As to the 114 cases succumbing to sudden fatal embolism not previously diagnosed, Zilliacus remarked that in most of them the diagnosis ought to have been made. Seventy of the patients were submitted to post-mortem examination and in 60 of them fresh thrombi were found in the deep veins of the lower extremity. In the remaining 10 cases the veins in the legs, the most common source of the emboli, were not examined.

Thus, according to Zilliacus, the fatal outcome of the unexpected pulmonary embolisms in this material could have been avoided in most of the cases by scrupulous daily examination of the lower extremities and the application of specific treatment. Only in the approximately 20 cases, where the primary cause of the thrombo-embolism was a fracture of the lower extremity, did plaster and bandages render an examination for signs of thrombosis more difficult. In practically all the other cases an early diagnosis ought to have been made and specific therapy given. As shown in table XX, the figure for the mortality from pulmonary embolism among the 576 cases receiving specific treatment was as low as 0.5 per cent, and among the 103 patients in table XXI, treated with anticoagulants, there were no deaths.

A total of 65 of these patients with pulmonary embolism without signs of thrombosis were treated conservatively. Of these patients 21 died, most of them after repeated attacks of embolism. Forty-four patients survived the attacks. These patients were in bed because of embolism for an average of 20 days and the temperature was raised for about 16 days.

A total of 103 cases were subjected to specific therapy. None of them died. Seventy-one patients were treated with heparin, 16 with heparin and dicumarol and 16 with dicumarol only. The 16 patients treated with dicumarol were in bed because of thrombosis for an average of 10.5 days and had pyrexia for 7.3 days. The time required for treating the patients in the two remaining groups was approximately the same.

These findings of Zilliacus clearly show that pulmonary

embolism should be treated with the specific anticoagulants as early and as adequately as possible.

In this particular case some hesitation may be felt because of the risk of haemorrhages into the pleural cavity from pulmonary infarctions (Falconer 1943, Keys and Schaffer 1942). The risk is, however, quite minimal and it is far outweighed by the risk of new attacks of pulmonary embolism. Every case of pulmonary embolism should be carefully treated because of the underlying peripheral thrombosis. It is even necessary to consider the possibility of thrombo-embolism in cases of pneumonia in which the diagnosis is uncertain. As will be discussed later, pneumonia with a temperature resistant to sulphonamides often reacts immediately to heparin treatment with a fall in temperature and recovery of the patient.

As to the choice of treatment, heparin is to be preferred and should be given in fairly large doses because of its immediate effect both on the peripheral source of the embolus and on the coagulative tendency of the blood in the obstructed pulmonary artery and its branches. It has been shown by radiography that emboli in the pulmonary artery can grow proximally (de Takats, Surg and Fowler 1945), giving rise to an increase in dyspnoea, pain and the area of dullness, which can be prevented by heparin.

The results reported by Zilliacus from Sweden can be supplemented by a series of *60 cases treated with heparin at the Drammen Hospital, Norway* (Liavaag and Nicolaysen 1946). There were 2 deaths, one of them before any treatment could be initiated. Recumbency lasted 9 days. Pyrexia for 8 days. Average doses of heparin per patient 2,350 mg. Haemorrhages occurred much more often than in the Swedish series.

Sequelae of Thrombosis.

The earlier literature contains little mention of the connection between ulcers of the leg and thrombophlebitis. Now it is known that the oedema, chronic induration and

ulcers are very often nothing but sequelae of thrombophlebitic processes in the deep veins of the leg, in the
popliteal and femoral veins (Leriche 1938, Homans 1938,
1939, p. 202, Bauer 1942).

Thrombosis has been shown to be the most important
aetiological factor in ulcers of the leg. In Sweden this
question has been studied from two aspects.

Birger, in 1941, in a dermatological study of 432 cases of
ulcers of the leg, found the primary cause of the disease
to be as follows:

Thrombosis . . 143 (33.0 %)	Undefined oedema . .	27
Phlebitis without	Erysipelas	3
varicose veins . 24 (5.6 %)	Oedema after fracture .	4
Phlebitis with	Trauma	29
	Diabetes	1
varicose veins . 89 (20.6 %)	Osteomyelitis	1
Varicose veins . 107 (24.8 %)	Deformity of the leg .	2
Other causes . . 69 (16 %)	Arteriosclerosis . . .	1
	Freezing	1
	Total	69

Thrombosis was thus found in 33 per cent and symptoms
of phlebitis in another 26 per cent. Varicose veins were
present in only 24 per cent.

Bauer (1942) studied the fate of cases of thrombosis by
means of phlebography. He noted ulcers of the leg to be
common in patients previously suffering from a thrombosis
in the deep veins of the thigh. After eliminating 6 cases
due to syphilis, tuberculosis or arteriosclerosis, he found, in
a series of 44 cases, that an earlier thrombosis of the deep
veins was the cause of ulcers of the leg in no less than 33
(87 %) of the remaining 38 cases.

In 1942, Willners found a history of thrombosis in 32
out of 73 cases of ulcers of the leg. In only 20 cases was
a previous thrombosis unlikely.

In a comprehensive paper in 1942 based on the phlebographic analysis of 145 cases of deep thrombosis Bauer
summarized his results as follows:

"After obliteration of the deep venous trunks of the leg by
thrombosis, the venous return from this region is taken over

permanently by an accessory venous system consisting solely of subcutaneous vessels, usually with the great saphenous vein as the main channel. As long as these subcutaneous veins are intact they are adequate for the return of blood from the lower leg. A mild venous stasis, however, is always present. This venous stasis causes chronic oedema of the lower leg, a finding present in all the cases of chronic obstruction by thrombosis.

The constant overload causes degeneration of the accessory system, the subcutaneous veins becoming dilated and tortuous and the valves defective. This degeneration brings with it an increase of venous congestion, the swelling of the lower leg becomes more pronounced. The chronic oedema gradually leads to the development of indurative changes.

In the centre of the indurated area, usually after the lapse of two or three years, an ulcer arises which as a rule persists unless therapeutic procedures are undertaken.

The ulcers are frequently attended by considerable pain and distress, the risk of infection is great and a fatal erysipelas may begin there."

Of one hundred persons with a history of deep-seated thrombosis of the leg, examined more than ten years later, all showed swelling of the leg. More than nine-tenths of them exhibited indurative changes and four-fifths had ulcers.

The interval between the acute thrombosis and the appearance of these symptoms is shown in Table XXII.

TABLE XXII

The Time of Onset of the Sequelae in 145 Conservatively Treated Cases of Deep-Seated Thrombosis of the Lower Leg and Thigh.
(Bauer 1942)

Times in years after onset of thrombosis	Number of cases	Oedema of lower leg		Induration		Ulceration	
		Present	Absent	Present	Absent	Present	Absent
Less than 1 year ..	8	8	—	—	8	—	8
1—5 years	26	26	—	17	9	4	22
5—10 years	12	12	—	9	3	7	5
More than 10 years	99	99	—	91	8	79	20
	145	145	—	117	28	90	55

Thus, among 145 cases of deep venous thrombosis of the lower leg and thigh, all of them developed oedema of the lower leg, 117 had induration and 90 ulcers. In most of them the severe complications developed late.

However, in another series of 111 patients with ulcers of the legs, 41 per cent of which were apparently due to a thrombosis, according to the history, Nilzén (1945) found that in 18 out of 43 patients with thrombosis, the ulcer had already appeared by the end of the first year.

These lesions, therefore, according to Bauer, should be called "*post-thrombotic ulcers*" instead of varicose ulcers.

Quite a different picture is obtained when we study the cases treated with heparin.

Out of 127 cases of thrombosis receiving early heparin treatment during 1940—43 at the Mariestad Hospital, 103 could be found in 1945 for a follow-up examination (Table XXIII). In 76 cases, that is three cases out of four, the thrombosis had remained localized in the calf. Eighty per cent of the 76 cases suffered no discomfort whatsoever in

TABLE XXIII

Sequelae 2—5 Years after Deep Venous Thrombosis (103 Cases)
Treated with Heparin at the Mariestad Hospital (1940—1943).
(Bauer 1946)

| | Swelling of the leg | | | | Heaviness and pains | |
| | Only in the calf | | | In the thigh | | |
Leg normal	Mild	Moderate	Severe		Moderate	Severe
Thrombosis limited to the calf 76 cases 60 (80 per cent)	16	—	—	—	2	—
Thrombosis in the calf and thigh 27 cases 14 (50 per cent)	3	8	2	5	—	3

their legs. In the remaining 20 per cent the symptoms were mild. Where the thrombus had extended to the thigh, half the patients suffered from marked swelling of the lower leg or the thigh and some of them from severe pain.

Bauer laid particular stress upon the necessity of detecting the thrombosis in its earliest stage while still in the lower leg, where its growth can be checked by means of early heparin therapy. If it spreads to the popliteal or the femoral vein a more or less advanced phlegmasia alba dolens will develop. Swelling, induration and ulcers may follow.

Because of the great significance of the sequelae of thrombosis both to the patients and the community, Zilliacus (1946), in his study, made a follow-up examination of as many of the patients as could be reached personally by himself or by mail. Of 790 cases referred to in table XX 601 were examined. To indicate clearly the different degrees of severity of the symptoms, he constructed a scale between one and eight as follows:

Index: Symptoms:

 I Subjectively and objectively fit.
 II Subjective disability (tenderness, pains, cramps, heaviness).
 III Subjective and objective disability after exertion (swelling, discoloration).
 IV Chronic swelling of the lower leg, or part of it.
 V Chronic discoloration, induration and enlarged varicose veins.
 VI Ulcus cruris.
 VII Swelling of the thigh after exertion.
 VIII Chronic swelling of the thigh.

The results of his follow-up examination are given in table XXIV.

As is evident from the table the index for the cases in which the thrombus had extended to the thigh is consistently higher than for the cases in which it had remained in the calf. For the conservatively treated patients where the thrombosis extended to the thigh the mean is 4.9. For the patients with thrombosis in the thigh receiving specific treatment the mean index is about the same, 4.5. The mean index for the cases with thrombosis in the calf treated with anticoagulants is 2.5.

Zilliacus found that only a few of the 132 conservatively treated patients were completely free from symptoms. Most of the patients followed in this group suffered from swelling in the calf (index 4) and from discoloration, induration or large varicose veins (index 5). Ulcera cruris were observed in 14 of the patients. In about 30 cases (not included in the table) in which the acute thrombosis had become bilateral, pains in both legs were recorded at the follow-up

TABLE XXIV

Sequelae in 790 Cases of Deep Venous Thrombosis given no Specific Treatment or Treated with Heparin, Heparin and Dicumarol or with Dicumarol alone at 19 Swedish Clinics (1940—1944). (Zilliacus 1946.)

Treatment		Number of cases (cases with sudden pulmonary embolism alone not included)	Follow-up examination Number of cases	Index of sequelae (mean)
No specific treatment	Calf	43 ⎫ 214 171 ⎭	132	4.9
	Thigh or calf and thigh..			
Heparin	Calf	155 ⎫ 342 187 ⎭	130	2.6
	Thigh or calf and thigh..		154	4.3
Heparin and dicumarol	Calf	40 ⎫ 103 63 ⎭ 266 (calf) 310 (thigh) 576	32	2.5
	Thigh or calf and thigh..		53	4.2
Dicumarol	Calf	71 ⎫ 131 60 ⎭	64	2.4
	Thigh or calf and thigh..		44	4.8
Total		790	602	

examination. In four of these ulcera cruris were bilateral. The mean index for this group, 1—5 years after the acute thrombosis, was approximately 5.

It was noted that when the thrombosis had extended to the thigh there was little difference between the conservatively treated cases and those treated with heparin. Swelling of the calf (index 4) and discolouration, induration with large varicose veins (index 5) were present in most of the cases of both groups. Ulcus cruris occurred in 11 of 154 such cases. The mean index for this group is at the same level as that among the conservatively treated cases i. e. 5. *An important difference, however, as compared with the conservatively treated cases, was that bilateral symptoms occurred only in 3 cases.*

The sequelae in the patients with thrombosis of the calf who were treated with heparin were generally mild. *66 out of 130 such cases were completely free from symptoms,* while the remaining patients showed only swelling of the calf after exertion. Only one patient in this group suffered from ulcer of the leg. The mean index was approximately 2.

In Zilliacus' material the sequelae were fully developed at the end of the first year and did not on the whole change during the following three years. *The specific therapy had, in cases where the thrombosis remained localized to the calf, permanently saved the patients from a chronic painful, more or less severe, disablement.*

Zilliacus found that in obstetric and gynaecological cases both *venous thrombosis and ulcers occur more frequently in the left leg than in the right.* In Nürnberger's (1934) 623 cases of thrombosis in the leg the lesion occurred on the left side in 72 per cent. Zilliacus (1946) found the thrombosis on the left side in 75 per cent of his 245 unilateral obstetric cases. Roholm (1937), who noted that ulcers of the leg occur three times more frequently in women than in men, stated that unilateral ulcers occurred on the left leg in 60.1 per cent of his 7,520 cases. These figures tend to show that the two conditions are associated.

It is beyond the scope of this monograph to enter into discussion on the extensive literature dealing with *the treatment of chronic induration and ulcers of the leg.* As the acute thrombosis not infrequently becomes a chronic condition with oedema the treatment applied at the end of the

11

hospitalization is important. In addition to the usual treatment with elastic bandages new principles have been applied
in recent years. Thus the Pavaex equipment, penicillin
and heparin have come into use. Thorsén (1945) modified
the Pavaex to a "Pressure-Pavaex" with an amplitude between + 60 and — 20 mm Hg instead of between + 20 and
— 80 mm Hg.

Trauma and thrombosis.

With the increased interest in thrombosis and its sequelae
a new problem has arisen in State Medicine. Since it has
become obvious that disabling swelling of the leg, induration
and ulcers very often follow a deep thrombosis which has
spread to the thigh, claims for damages will soon be made
on the accident insurance companies or on the State Health
Insurance Fund, in cases where thrombosis has appeared
after a trauma. It is, in fact, a common occurrence for a
deep thrombosis to follow trauma both to the upper and
especially to the lower extremities. All the consequences,
inclusive of invalidity, following the thrombosis can be
directly ascribed to the acute trauma.

In 1934 Vance called attention to the high frequency of
thrombosis following leg injuries, not only severe ones but
also after simple fractures of the fibula and very mild
lesions and injuries to the soft tissue. Here the local symp-

TABLE XXV

*Incidence of a History of Trauma amongst Cases of Thrombosis
at the Mariestad Hospital*

	No. of cases	No. of cases developing thrombosis	Incidence of thrombosis
Total no. of patients ad- mitted	9,281	127	1.37 %
Traumatic conditions in lower extremities	276	33	11.9 %
Other patients	9,005	94	1.04 %

toms, the swelling, and the pain on pressure make diagnosis difficult. In uncertain cases venography may be extremely valuable. In 1944 Bauer studied 127 cases of deep venous thrombosis by means of venography. In them he found that thrombosis was twelve times more common among cases of leg injuries than in all the rest of the material. (Table XXV.)

An approximately similar frequency of thrombosis was reported by Jacob (1945) from Switzerland. In 120 cases with fractures in the lower leg there were 10 cases of thrombosis (8.3 per cent).

Consequently, the disability following thrombosis of the leg can in many cases be traced back to trauma of some kind and claims will be made for annuities to be paid to the disabled patients or in the case of a fatal outcome to their relatives.

Complications of Heparin Treatment.

Haemorrhages.

The formation of haematomata is the most common and the most serious complication following heparin treatment. It is not unusual during prophylactic post-operative heparinization. Haematomata in the wound appear frequently during the post-operative course. In vascular surgery particularly, the tendency to bleed is very pronounced. An oozing from the suture canals in the wall of the sutured vessels is reported by Lindgren and Wilander.

The tendency to bleed is very pronounced if the heparin is given too early. Thus König in Germany, in 1942, observed haemorrhages at the site of the operation in 9 out of 100 cases. He gave 100 mg. of heparin immediately after the conclusion of the operation.

Contrary to the findings in post-operative prophylactic heparin treatment, the tendency to bleed very seldom causes trouble when spontaneous thrombosis and pulmonary embolism are treated with heparin. No complicating haemorrhages due to the heparin occurred in the series of Bauer, Hellsten, Crafoord and Wetterdal, comprising more than

600 cases, including those with pulmonary embolism. Similarly, 150 cases of retinal thrombosis treated by Ploman, Rosengren, Larsson and Måhlén with fairly large doses of heparin, 300—400 mg. a day for 10 to 15 days, showed no serious complications. Almost all these patients received the heparin in single injections, causing a considerable increase in the coagulation time of the blood, which might seem to involve a more direct risk than the continuous infusion method. In a few patients a transient haematuria occurred during the heparin treatment, a finding which has also been reported by Murray, by Ershler and Blaisdell and by Priestly, Essex and Barker. In most of these patients the treatment was not interrupted, in spite of the discolouration of the urine.

The only complication reported following heparin treatment for thrombo-embolism is haemorrhage into the pleural cavity from pulmonary infarctions. Falconer described two cases in 1943. In the first case a totally inadequate dose of heparin had been given. The patient suddenly died from pulmonary embolism. One litre of blood was found in the pleural cavity. In the second case an excessive dose of 750 mg. of heparin a day was given for five days. A haemorrhage into the pleural cavity amounting to 1,200 ml. was considered to be the cause of death. In 1942 Keyes and Schaffer at the Henry Ford Hospital, Detroit, reporting 60 cases treated with heparin, described two in which there was bloody fluid in the pleural cavity after pulmonary infarction. They did not consider this outweighed the value of the treatment.

According to the experience gained in the Swedish clinics, this complication is very rare and usually caused by excessive doses of heparin. The risk should not be exaggerated, because the development of the exudate in the pleural cavity can easily be followed and, if necessary, checked. *In any event, the conclusion should not be drawn that heparin cannot be given in case of pulmonary embolism with signs of infarction, because the thrombosis of the deep veins underlying every case of pulmonary embolism is per se a much more serious danger.*

The first step in checking a significant haemorrhage is to withdraw the heparin. In case of need, a blood transfusion is given. The coagulation time then quickly returns to normal. If an immediate effect is desirable, *protamine sulphate* is given intravenously: 5 to 10 ml. of a sterile 1 per cent solution *brings the coagulation time of the blood instantaneously to normal*. The pure protamine sulphate from herring or salmon is dissolved in dilute hydrochloride acid, pH 3, and sterilized in an autoclave. It produces no undesirable reactions.

Toxicity.

The non-toxicity of the purified commercial heparin has been claimed repeatedly. In rabbits no toxic reactions occur after single intravenous doses of 500 mg. nor after repeated injections of 10 mg. per kilo of body weight. Post-mortem examination of the parenchymatous organs of a patient who died of coronary thrombosis after receiving a total of 11 gm. of heparin in 7 days revealed no histological changes whatsoever.

True anaphylactic reactions occurred in four patients in the above-mentioned Swedish series. A serious shock occurred in one of them when the treatment was taken up again after an interval of one week. The tendency to sensitization, however, is not by any means so pronounced as it is with the anti-anaemic liver preparations. In any case, it may be advisable to start the treatment with a small dose e. g. 25 mg. of heparin in order to unmask any possible allergic hypersensitivity of the patient.

The anaphylactic reaction with its typical symptoms following immediately after an injection should not be confused with toxic reactions, such as the chills, pyrexia, severe headache and ache in the lumbar region caused by less pure heparin preparations. These symptoms do not appear immediately, but within one or two hours after the injection. Once the impurities causing the reaction are removed from the heparin the treatment seems to be harmless.

Treatment of Thrombosis of the Retinal Veins.

The first attempt to use heparin in acute venous thrombosis in man was made in a case of thrombosis of the central vein of the retina. In 1937 Holmin (Holmin and Ploman 1938) tried the new anticoagulant in an acute case of retinal thrombosis in a young person and noted during the next days an improvement in visual acuity and a quick disappearance of the haemorrhages. Here the results of the treatment could be observed directly.

Shortly afterwards Boström and William-Olsson (1938) reported a similar case. Ploman reported further cases in 1938. After that, practically all cases of retinal thrombosis occurring at most of the hospitals in Sweden during the following years were treated with heparin, not so much because of any encouraging results, but mainly in order to find out whether the treatment was of value or not. The · results were discussed by Ploman, Rosengren, Larsson and Måhlén at a meeting of the Swedish Ophthalmological Society in June, 1942.

At this meeting Ploman reported on not less than 81 cases of retinal thrombosis treated with heparin, a dose of 150 mg. twice a day for ten days being usually given. In 40 of the cases the thrombosis was in the tributary veins.

Of 41 cases with *thrombosis in the trunk of the central vein*, 38 were re-examined after about two years. Twenty-one of them showed improvement, the visual acuity being on the average 0.8 as compared with the initial figure of 0.3. Four of them were unchanged and 13 were worse. In 8 cases the ocular tension had risen and in 4 cases secondary glaucoma necessitated enucleation.

Of the 40 cases with *thrombosis in the tributary veins*, 14 were improved (visual acuity on the average 0.4 before the treatment and 0.8 on re-examination), 12 were unchanged and 5 got worse. In no less than 15 patients a central chorioiditis was present on re-examination. In one case secondary glaucoma necessitated enucleation of the eye. In 9 out of the re-examined 31 cases vision was completely restored, 6 could read, 14 could see to walk and 2 became blind.

Even in the improved cases, however, sinuous veins, un-eveness in calibre, and thickening of the walls developed both in the vein and in its concomitant artery. As a rule, the other eye also, in these cases, showed vascular alterations concomitant with the increased blood pressure. The mean age of the 31 patients in the last group was 62 years, only one of them being younger than 50 years. Almost all showed raised blood pressure. In the first group of 38 re-examined patients, only 7 were younger than 50 years and about 70 per cent showed hypertension. The general impression was that younger people benefited more from the treatment than the older ones did.

In Gothenburg, Rosengren applied the principles intro-duced by Ploman. His material comprised 30 cases (Rosen-gren and Stenström 1942). Because of the undefined pic-ture and the uncertain prognosis of this syndrome, par-ticularly when the thrombosis is in the tributary veins, which was the case in 20 of his patients, Rosengren con-sidered it difficult to make any definite statements about the value of heparin treatment. If, however, the visual acuity is taken as a measure of the changes occurring in the eye, then there was an immediate improvement following the heparin treatment. The mean initial visual acuity of the 30 cases was 0.239, and 10 days later, after finishing the treatment, the mean was 0.375. The difference, 0.136 ± 0.054, is real. Such an immediate change in the visual acuity is not known to occur normally. Furthermore, if the patients are re-examined after 2—4 weeks no further improvement is noted; on the contrary, the state is unchanged or a retro-gression has taken place. Of his 30 patients 21 were im-proved during the time of the heparin treatment and 4 remained unchanged. During the next 2—4 weeks after the termination of the treatment only 7 out of 26 cases were improved and 9 remained unchanged. Rosengren pointed out that no glaucoma occurred among his cases.

The daily dose of heparin was 250 mg. in 10 cases, a fairly small dose, and 350 mg. in the others.

Larsson reported on 31 cases. In 19 cases the thrombus was in the trunk of the central vein. In 7 of the cases where the initial visual acuity had been 0.1, 1.0, 0.9, 0.2, 0.4, 0.3, 0.4, the final mean figure on re-examination after 14—44 months was 1.0. Larsson described the pathology of this syndrome. He pointed out that vascular changes are common and that these patients often had earlier apoplectic fits caused by cerebral haemorrhage or arterial spasm. Hypertension occurs in most of the patients. Because of arterial constriction the flow of blood in the retinal vessels is slowed. It is very likely that the picture of the retinal thrombosis in many cases is not caused by thrombosis but by an impaired circulation due to arterial spasm or partial vascular obliteration, hence the irregular course of this condition.

Måhlén reported on 11 cases of thrombosis in the trunk of the central vein and 7 cases with the lesion in the tributary veins. In the first group 8 showed improvement, in the second group 6 of them. No secondary glaucoma developed. The final visual acuities in the first group, were 1, 0.5, 0.5, 0.4, 0.4, 0.2 and 0.1 and in the second group 1, 1, 0.7, 0.6, 0.6, 0.2 and 0.1. A further 8 cases with haemorrhages in the eyegrounds were heparinized and in some of these the reabsorption proceeded unusually quickly.

Thus 148 cases of retinal "venous thrombosis" treated with heparin were reported by the Swedish authors. Of 68 cases in which the process was located in the trunk of the central vein improvement was reported during the course of the treatment in 36 cases. Out of 38 cases of thrombosis in the tributary veins, 20 were reported as improved. Out of 30 other cases where no distinction as to the localization had been made, 21 showed improvement. Among Ploman's 69 re-examined cases, 20 regained normal vision, 15 a visual acuity of 0.4—0.8, 20 of 0.3 or less, and 14 went blind. Enucleation for glaucoma was reported by Ploman in 5 cases but in no case by the other authors.

As to the value of the heparin treatment, Ploman, referring to papers by Odquist (1942) and by Jensen (1936), calls attention to the fact that spontaneous improvement and complete recovery are seen in this disease irrespective of the location of the thrombus. Nevertheless he considers the immediate improvement in the visual acuity in so many cases would not otherwise be expected and indicates that heparin treatment has a favourable influence. The relatively few cases with secondary glaucoma, 8 out of 38 cases with thrombosis in the trunk of the central vein, provide a further point in favour of the treatment. Ploman gives his opinion of its value in the discussion as to which patients should receive heparin. Even if he considers it difficult to give a final answer to this question, his experience seems to provide some guidance in selecting the cases. "It is obviously of no use to treat patients with so-called complete thrombosis in which the papilla is wholly obliterated by massive haemorrhages extending far out toward the periphery and concealing the macular region; nor is it worth while treating eyes in which increased macular tension has already occurred. In no cases in which this feature was present in my series was any improvement or decrease of the tension achieved. But impairment of vision ought not to be taken as the only deciding factor. Even a low visual acuity sometimes improves rapidly during the course of the treatment. The general appearance of the retinal lesions should be the final criterion; if it is fairly easy to see the papilla, and if the haemorrhages and white foci of degeneration are not too extensive, it is worth trying heparin treatment."

As to the dosage of heparin used by Ploman some supplementary notes are necessary. The amount of heparin usually given, 300 mg. a day, either 3×100 mg. or 2×150 mg., was chosen at a very early date. Later, the experiences of Bauer and of Hellsten showed this dose to be too small for the treatment of thrombosis in persons of normal weight, 400—450 mg. a day of the Swedish standard heparin being desirable at least during the first 3—4 days and divided into 3 or 4 injections. Possibly an increased dose of heparin, e. g. $125 + 100 (75) + 100 (75) + 125$ mg. of heparin daily, would improve the results in these patients also, without much increasing the tendency to bleed.

So far Ploman and his colleagues have observed only local haemorrhages at the site of injection. The larger dose of heparin might possibly increase the tendency to bleed. The first injection of heparin should be not more than 25 mg. The remainder of the first dose can then be given when it is certain that there is no hypersensitivity.

The question of the use of heparin in retinal venous thrombosis has been discussed further by Ferguson (1941), Kravitz (1942), Rychener (1942), Levison and Roberts (1942), Rosenthal and Guzch (1943) and by Ciotola (1945).

A case of embolism in the retinal artery treated with heparin has been reported by Quist (1943). Treatment with 2×100 mg. of heparin a day was started on the sixth day and continued for 12 days. In general, no effect is observed in the treatment of occluding arterial embolism with heparin. But in this case there was a slight improvement.

Treatment of Mesenteric Thrombosis with Heparin.

Particular attention has been paid to the treatment of mesenteric thrombosis with heparin. In this disease the effect of the treatment with heparin is very easy to ascertain because the mortality is very high, almost 100 per cent in cases not subjected to operation. Zweigbergk (1942) found in the cases submitted to operation a mortality of 85 per cent. Without operation, mortality was 90—95 per cent. Luke (1943) refers to material collected by Cokkinis in which 39 out of 40 conservatively treated cases died. A somewhat lower mortality was found by Ficarra (1944), 60—90 per cent of 554 cases collected from the literature.

Murray and MacKenzie reported in 1939 six consecutive patients who were given heparin following the resection of from one to two metres of intestine because of mesenteric thrombosis. Four of them recovered. The two other patients were treated in the same way but one of them died of pneumonia and the other of an advanced peritonitis. In the former case the postmortem examination revealed no pathological changes in the abdominal cavity.

Similarly, Ravdin in 1941 treated two cases of mesenteric thrombosis with heparin. Both patients recovered without resection although there were clinical signs of massive involvement of the intestine.

In Sweden three cases have been published and four other cases are known. Of the seven patients five recovered. As early as 1937 a patient, aged 56, was successfully treated by the resection of 20 cm. of intestine and heparinization with a dose of 150 mg. four times daily for three days (Zweigbergk 1937). In 1942 Rudberg gave heparin to a patient, aged 61, when the symptoms were fairly advanced but no resection was made, because the intestine seemed viable. Laparotomy revealed thrombi in the mesenteric veins. The patient received 4×125 mg. of heparin daily for three days, 4×100 mg. on each of the next two days, 3×75 mg. daily during the next week and smaller doses for still another week. Between the second and the fourth day a marked change occurred in the condition of the patient and recovery followed.

Murray recommends heparin prophylactically after splenectomy after which portal thrombosis is known to occur. In 1942 Murray and MacKenzie had given heparin to 11 patients after splenectomy without any signs of postoperative thrombosis.

In 1944 Lichtenstein reported a case of mesenteric thrombosis, an 11-year old boy who had suffered for 5 years from ulcerative colitis and was very anaemic. He suddenly became ill with a temperature, vomiting and abdominal pains located to the spleen, which was palpable. In a few days signs of thrombosis developed, first in the left leg and then in the right. The superficial veins of the abdomen were clearly visible. There was ascites and oedema of both legs and in the scrotum. His condition was considered hopeless. Tentatively 6×25 mg. of heparin were given daily for a week. In a few days a change was noticed and in a fairly short time all the symptoms receded. The recovery of the patient was considered to be due to the heparin treatment.

Laufmann in 1942 studied the effect of heparin in dogs with infarction of the intestine after strangulation, mesenteric thrombosis and other vascular obstruction. He noted that the heparin had a definite although slight effect in these conditions. If vessels supplying 15 to 20 cm. of the intestine were ligated or thrombosed, the result was gangrene, irrespective of whether heparin was given to the animals or not. In the heparinized dogs there was a better blood supply to the intestine and they tolerated destruction of the afferent and efferent vessels from some 10 or 12 cm. more of the intestine than did the untreated animals. It was found necessary to resect the corresponding part of the intestine as soon as the vessels were occluded, as otherwise gangrene followed. The chance of recovery when segments of the intestine have been deprived of their blood supply in occlusion of the mesenteric vessels or in strangulation is very small, even if the area is limited. Heparin therefore should not be administered in cases of impaired circulation of the intestine unless resection is performed. Once this is done, heparin can be given, due attention being paid to careful haemostasis.

Laufman found that heparin was dangerous, if administered shortly after strangulation of the intestine, causing death in almost all the dogs. They died of shock due to loss of blood and fluid into the peritoneal cavity and the lumen of the intestine. The dogs not given heparin recovered.

A similar sequence of events was observed by Crafoord and by Wetterdal in two fatal cases treated post-operatively with prophylactic doses of heparin. Evidently the heparinization facilitated the exudation of blood and tissue fluid into the peritoneal cavity as in the case of the dogs.

The experimental findings of Laufman, taken together with the clinical observations of Crafoord and of Wetterdal, make it desirable to watch patients given heparin after major intra-abdominal operations much more carefully than after other operations.

Luke (1943) discusses the possibility of giving heparin to patients with mesenteric thrombosis, due attention being paid to the experimental findings of Laufman in dogs. In spite of these results, it is evident that early cases of mesenteric venous thrombosis, where the intestine, although distended, oedematous and discoloured, still seems to be viable, should not be submitted to intestinal resection but should be given adequate heparin treatment. He described an instructive case with serious abdominal symptoms. On laparotomy the mesenteric veins were found to be thrombosed as in Rudberg's case. The intestine was apparently viable. The abdomen was therefore closed and heparin was given for ten days in a continuous infusion, 10,000 Toronto units per litre, 25—30 drops per minute. The coagulation time was checked by the capillary tube method every 6 hours and kept at about 15 minutes. The patient recovered quickly.

The instructive experience of Murray and his co-workers and the three cases of Rudberg, Luke and Lichtenstein clearly indicate that heparin is of extraordinary value in the treatment of mesenteric venous thrombosis, at least in its earlier stages.

Thrombosis in the Cavernous Sinus.

The history and the clinical picture of thrombosis in the cavernous sinus has recently been reviewed by MacNeal, Frisbee and Beevins (1943).

Several cases of this disease, formerly known to have a very severe course, have recently been cured by chemotherapy or penicillin combined with an adequate dose of heparin. It is probable that the heparinization, which is known to exert an inhibitory effect in venous thrombosis, in these cases also hastened the process of recovery. Thus Lyons (1941) treated two consecutive cases of serious staphylococcal sinus cavernosus thrombophlebitis of the anterior type with chemotherapeutics, sulphapyridine, sulphathiazole and heparin. Sulphathiazole was given in dosages sufficient to maintain a blood level of 5 mg. per cent and heparin was given in intravenous infusion, 2.25 gm. during 17 days to one of the patients and 5.8 gm. between the fourth and the nineteenth day to the others. 20,000 Toronto units (200 mg.) of heparin were added to 1,500 ml. of isotonic saline or glucose solution and administered by constant intravenous infusion. Bacteriaemia persisted for 6 and 8 days and after ten days the most serious clinical symptoms had abated. The intracranial infection persisted for many weeks and was held in check by chemotherapy alone. Both patients recovered. Schall (1941) reported on a third similar case from the same clinic successfully treated in the same way. Ershler and Blaisdell (1941) published a similar case.

A very severe case of cavernous sinus thrombosis was successfully treated with heparin and sulphonamides by Renvall, in 1945, after an ineffective treatment with sulphonamides alone for four days. The patient, a 16-year old girl, had the typical symptoms of sinus thrombosis. After four days sulphapyrimidine and sulphathiazole were given intravenously. During the next four days, the patient got much worse and was in a very bad condition with severe meningitic symptoms. Cells in the cerebrospinal fluid 50,000, *but no bacteria*. Temperature 39.2° C. Marked exophthalmus, haemorrhages and ulcerations on the conjunctivae and a swollen face. At the suggestion of G. Bauer, she was then given for 10 days sulphonamides every four hours and 150 mg. of heparin intravenously every six hours. There was a marked change. All the symptoms abated in a week. After four days there were only 530 cells/mm^3 in the cerebrospinal fluid and after 10 days the temperature was almost normal. Complete recovery followed except for slight persistent protrusion of the eyes. In this case, the influence of the anticoagulant therapy is clear, since sulphonamides alone had given no relief. The high dosage of heparin, 600 mg. a day, was considered necessary.

In 1944 Wiesenfeld and Phillips treated a case in which a staphylococcal infection following extraction of teeth in a young man thrombosed the cavernous sinus. Recovery followed under penicillin and heparin therapy.

In these particular cases, where the symptoms of thrombosis were so prominent, it is very likely that the administration of heparin was an essential factor in the recovery.

That penicillin therapy alone can be sufficient was shown in one case by Johnstone, 1945. In another case reported by Muntarbhorn sulphathiazole was given in conjunction with heparin.

Martin (1941) gave a thorough description of the clinical picture of thrombosis in the superior longitudinal sinus following childbirth. No specific treatment was, however, given in his three cases.

Stansfield in 1942 reported on two such cases. On the 9th day after parturition one of them, aged 25 years, developed nervous symptoms, hemianopia and epileptiform fits. She was given *200 mg. of heparin* intravenously every four hours in a pint of 5 per cent glucose. She recovered. According to Stansfield early diagnosis now enables us to combat this otherwise invariably fatal complication of the puerperium. "The survival of the patient will be the clinican's reward for an early diagnosis."

The Treatment of Subacute Bacterial Endocarditis with Heparin.

Because of the seriousness of the *Streptococcus viridans* infection all available therapeutic means, amongst them heparin, have been tried in the endeavour to find a cure. The object in using heparin has been to assist first sulphonamide and later on penicillin therapy. It was assumed that the lessened coagulability of the blood would counteract the formation of fibrin clots on the valves of the heart, thus making the pathogenic bacteria more accessible to the sterilizing influence of the blood.

The theoretical ground for this treatment, however, is not very convincing. In spite of the non-coagulability of the blood a further formation of membranes might take place through exudation from the ulcerated parts of the valves. This is what actually occurs. Thus after treating a patient with heparin alone, Fletcher in 1941 observed on postmortem examination fresh fibrin clots on the valves, the usual finding in these cases. Despite the intensive use of heparin over a long period, Oldfeldt in 1942 made a similar observation in one case.

The alleged beneficial effects of heparin treatment in this disease might also be due to spontaneous remissions such as have been observed by different authors even without sulphonamide therapy. (Lichtman and Bierman 1941.)

Heparin was first suggested by Friedman, Hamburger and Katz in 1939. Kelson and White in the same year claimed to have seen a beneficial effect after treating 7 patients. In 3 cases, however, the intravenous heparin treatment was not tolerated at all, and in 2 cases for three days only. None of them received heparin for more than a week. Leach, Faulkner, Duncan, Mc Ginn, Porter and White, in 1941, reported 41 cases treated regularly with different sulphonamide preparations: 4, or 10 per cent, of the patients recovered.

In this disease, in which infected thrombotic emboli are very common, the course of the cerebral emboli is aggravated by haemorrhages following the heparin treatment. Complications of this kind have been reported by Friedman, Hamburger, and Katz (1939), Witts (1940), Miller (1940), Fletcher (1940 and 1941), and Dockeray and Kawerau (1940).

In order to study the value of this treatment, Oldfeldt in 1942 submitted three typical cases with bacteriaemia to a very thorough prolonged heparin treatment combined with sulphapyridine and sulphathiazole therapy. One of them died from subdural haemorrhages in connection with the treatment. In another case the autopsy revealed a cerebral haemorrhage around a local thrombo-embolic ramollissement, and fresh fibrinous masses on the heart valves, thus demonstrating the complete ineffectiveness of the treatment. Warburg (1942) observed no effect of the heparin in 5 cases.

McLean, Meyer and Griffith (1941) summarized from the literature 67 cases of subacute bacterial endocarditis treated with heparin. They considered further trials with the drug in this disease almost unnecessary, at least along the lines hitherto applied. In regard to the method of administering the heparin they found the intravenous infusion of huge quantities of fluid unsuitable in these patients with a badly damaged heart.

The value of heparin in this disease was also denied by Friedman (1941) and by Fletcher (1941 b).

With the introduction of *penicillin therapy* the first positive results in the treatment of subacute bacterial endocarditis have been obtained (See Loewe et. al. 1944). The literature on this subject is steadily increasing. It is beyond the scope of this monograph to enter into discussion on this question. There seems to be very little use, if any at all, for anticoagulants in this disease.

Heparin treatment without penicillin is contra-indicated in thrombosis of the pelvic veins due to puerperal sepsis with septicaemia.

In puerperal sepsis, where an infection has penetrated the wall of the pelvic or iliac veins causing thrombosis, heparin is contra-indicated. Here the thrombus formation is a protective mechanism preventing the spread of the infection by the blood stream. It is repeatedly observed (Simon 1943) that the septicaemia is brought to an end and the bacteria first disappear from the blood when a local thrombosis arises in the affected veins. With the introduction of penicillin therapy the situation has changed. It seems reasonable to apply anticoagulants to control the thrombosis as soon as the septicaemia is overcome.

Anticoagulants in the Treatment of Post-Traumatic, Arteriosclerotic, Diabetic and Frostbite Gangrene.

A decreased coagulability of the blood is obviously valuable for the nutrition of the tissues in semi-gangrenous parts of the extremities. Anticoagulant therapy seems therefore to be indicated after trauma, in frostbite or in diabetic gangrene of the most peripheral parts of the extremities.

Particularly in diabetic gangrene, a combined heparin and penicillin therapy has proved to be of utmost value (Sedwitz[1]). The beneficial influence of anticoagulant

---

[1] Personal communication to the author.

12

therapy in frostbite was convincingly demonstrated by Loewe et. al., 1945 and by Lange and Loewe, 1946. Frostbite was induced in man and animals and treated with heparin. Referring to papers of previous authors (Kreyberg and Rotnes 1932, Greene 1943 and Lange and Boyd 1945) they stated that local freezing at first results in a diffusion of plasma into the perivascular spaces and a concentration and agglutination of the cellular elements within the blood vessels. After about 72 hours these cells are organized into thrombi and this ultimately leads to gangrene.

In rabbits parts of the skin exposed to solid carbon dioxide for more than 15 minutes became gangrenous if the animals were not given heparin within 4 hours of the exposure. One hind leg of each of the rabbits was kept at -12—$20°$ C $(10.4$—$4°$ F) for 45 to 90 minutes. The legs including the bones were lost. Among the 11 rabbits receiving heparin only slight surface lesions were observed in two of them.

Similar experiments were made on human volunteers, the skin being exposed to solid carbon dioxide either once for ten minutes or twice for 30 minutes at six day intervals. All the adequately heparinized cases escaped any lesions. The heparin was given subcutaneously in single large doses, 300 mg., in the Pitkin gelatine medium.

The authors also reported the case of a man left on the street at $-5°$ C for 14 hours with his hands unprotected and his feet protected only by thin socks and low shoes. He was given heparin by the intravenous route for five days and escaped permanent tissue loss, which was much better than the result expected without anticoagulant therapy.

Brambel and Loker (1944) reported 11 such cases with more or less severe crush injuries in four cases, diabetic gangrene of the foot in three cases and frostbite in one case. In all of them amputations seemed unavoidable, but improvement followed without amputation after treatment with dicumarol. The acute cases were treated for only a few days, the chronic ones for two or even three months with a total quantity of dicumarol amounting to 4—5 grams. Heparin was given at the beginning to some of them, 200 mg. in one litre of saline for 18 hours.

The use of heparin for complications due to sclerosing of varicose veins.

After massive retrograde injection of a sclerosing agent such as sodium ricinoleate into superficial varicose veins, marked swelling of the entire leg, tenderness and discoloration of the skin over the veins, cramp-like pains and an impaired circulation are often noted (Sedwitz 1942). In cases where there are bunches of grape-like varices along the whole length of the saphenous vein, preventing the passage of the catheter, Sedwitz recommends venous ligation with subsequent multiple injections of sclerosing material along the course of the vein. In fourteen such cases he injected heparin, 100 mg. every four hours, intravenously, the patient being kept as ambulant as possible with the legs wrapped in an elastic bandage. The pain was relieved in most cases four hours after the first injection of heparin and never later than after the second injection. There was a marked change in the course of the condition, because without heparin the symptoms increased in severity for two or three days and the patient was kept in hospital for two to three weeks. Recovery was not complete until at least a month later.

The Prevention of Pleural and Peritoneal Adhesions with Heparin.

A prerequisite for the formation of adhesions in the pleural and peritoneal cavities is the admixture of fibrinogen to the serous exudate following infections in these cavities or mechanical injury to the serous membranes. Once fibrin is formed the fluid cannot be easily reabsorbed. The fibrin acts as a foreign body stimulating the accumulation of cellular elements and organization takes place.

The process of organization thus depends on the transformation of fibrinogen to fibrin. Consequently, it should be prevented if heparin is administered locally. This is what actually occurs.

The extensive literature dealing with the experimental and clinical work on the prophylaxis of peritoneal adhesions in man and in animals has recently been summarized by Boys (1942). Since heparin is the only therapeutic agent which at present offers promise in the prophylaxis of this important complication in abdominal surgery, this question is of general interest. Animal experiments have given most promising results.

In 1935, Miki and Satani found that introduction of a solution of heparin in saline into the peritoneal cavity of rabbits "considerably precluded" intraperitoneal adhesions after scarification of the duodenal and omental serosae with dry gauze. In 1936, Widström and Wilander tried to prevent pleural adhesions in rabbits by introducing pure heparin solution into the pleural cavity. Pleuritis was induced by injecting iodine. At autopsy on the third or sixth day a copius pleural exudate with fibrin threads and membranes was found consistently. When 10 mg. or more of heparin a day had been injected into the pleural cavity the exudate remained fluid or was reabsorbed.

A most extensive study of the prevention of peritoneal adhesions in rabbits and dogs was published by Lehman and Boys in 1940. Adhesions were produced either by a mechanical trauma to the peritoneum or by bacterial contamination. If 750 Toronto units of heparin were introduced into the abdominal cavity of the rabbit on two consecutive days no adhesions were found after a week, whereas all the control rabbits receiving saline or amniotic fluid showed adhesions. If the adhesions produced in the same way in dogs were divided, still more new threads and membranes developed in the course of two weeks. If normal saline or amniotic fluid or saline with 3000 units of heparin were injected by paracentesis on the first and second post-operative day after division of the adhesions, no re-formation of adhesions occurred in the dogs receiving heparin.

These experiments of Lehman and Boys, further extended in 1942 to comprise a total of 170 experiments on dogs, obviously offer considerable promise for abdominal surgery in the future. The formation of adhesions after peritoneal infections is a very important complication which may cause obstruction and strangulation of the intestine. It seems probable that these sequelae of infection or surgical operations may be prevented in the future when an efficient technique of administering heparin has been elaborated, at least as an adjunct to penicillin therapy. They originate from an acute lesion of the peritoneum during the course of which the exudate could be kept incoagulable by means of heparin.

Inflammation causing pleural adhesions, unlike that in the peritoneum, has a protracted course and is therefore less suitable for this treatment.

Intra-abdominal administration of heparin, however, is complicated by a tendency to intra-abdominal haemorrhage. In dogs with fresh granulation tissue, this bleeding may be severe enough to cause death. This tendency to bleed into the peritoneal cavity was also observed by Laufmann (1942) in intravenously heparinized dogs after strangulation of the intestine, and by Crafoord and Wetterdal during prophylactic post-operative heparin treatment in man. In a few cases the peritoneal cavity was filled with a sanguineous exudate. The only fatal complications in patients treated with heparin were of this type.

Patients treated by intra-peritoneal injection of heparin must therefore be observed extremely carefully for symptoms indicating a loss of blood. The coagulation time of the blood ought to be determined at two to four hour intervals and before a dose of heparin. Heparin should not be used when granulation or subacute inflammatory tissue is present. In 1941 Lehman and Boys described the results of treating 14 patients with heparin intra-peritoneally. One of them died and another had an alarming drop in the blood count. In 11 cases no ill effects were observed. Before and after giving heparin intra-peritoneally painstaking measures of precaution were taken, and are described in detail by the authors. A review of the surgical measures for the prevention and treatment of peritoneal adhesions was made by Boys (1942).

It is very questionable whether heparin will assist in preventing adhesions in joints. The injection of the drug involves a risk of infecting the synovial fluid, which would make the situation still worse.

Heparin has also been injected intra-cardially in pericarditis. In some cases where the injections were performed with a very fine needle no discomfort was experienced. In one patient, however, a haemorrhage followed, resulting in heart tamponade.

The effect of heparin in preventing fibrin formation in inflammatory exudates resulting in organization and fibrosis has been utilized by Boys and Harris to lessen the inflammation which follows roentgen irradiation damage to the lungs in experiments on rabbits. They found less injury to the lungs.

Heparin in Vascular Surgery.

The regional and general use of heparin has considerably increased the scope of vascular surgery. Operations on the blood vessels are always more or less liable to cause thrombosis. Thus the formation of secondary thrombi often spoils the results of late arterial embolectomies. In the old days, arterial embolism of 10—12 hours' standing was very likely to cause gangrene. Other kinds of operations on the vessels, such as the resection of aneurysms and suture of major arterial lesions, although technically possible, used to be very difficult to carry out. Our potentialities in surgical achievements have now been considerably improved, as Murray at the Toronto General Hospital has demonstrated in such an excellent way.

The beneficial influence of heparin on healing in vascular surgery was demonstrated by Murray and Best in 1938. When the axillary, femoral and carotid arteries of dogs were cut and sutured with silk they remained patent in 80 per cent of the animals when regional heparinization was used but in only 35 per cent without heparin. Artificial emboli were left in place for 24 to 72 hours and successfully removed from the arteries in every one of 8 dogs. In 9 dogs not treated with heparin the vessels became occluded in every instance. The same success was obtained in performing venous grafts, when segments of one and a half to three inches of the carotid and other arteries were excised and replaced by grafts from the jugular vein.

This experience has also been applied in man by Murray, who in 1941 reported several cases of end-to-end suture of arteries, resections of arterio-venous fistulas with repair of the vessels and restoration of normal circulation, 4 instances of venous graft and 17 cases of arterial embolectomy. In one case a popliteal aneurysm was resected and the gap was bridged with a $3\,^1/_4$ inch graft from the external jugular vein. The venous grafts healed and were able to function as parts of the arteries. The effect of heparin was carefully controlled and the coagulation time was kept at about 15 minutes.

Murray and Janes, in 1940, discussed the further possibility of preventing failure of the peripheral circulation in injuries to the larger arteries. The circulation can be maintained temporarily by the insertion of a glass cannula kept patent by the use of heparin. In dogs, Tuffier tubes of 1.5—2 mm. bore and 3.5 cm. length were placed between the cut ends of the common carotid artery. Applied to man, this principle will certainly become useful, enabling patients to be transported to hospitals where permanent repair or bridging of the gap by venous grafts may be carried out.

In the papers of Murray and Best, and of Murray (1940 a, b, c), particular attention was drawn to the possibility of performing late arterial embolectomies under heparinization. In the first paper they reported a successful removal of emboli from both the common iliac and femoral arteries 25 hours after the first appearance of the symptoms. Two of the 17 cases reported upon in the second paper had a completely obstructing embolus at the bifurcation of the aorta.

Lindgren, in 1939, described a similar case with embolism of the abdominal aorta, iliacs, and right and left femorals, which he operated upon 32 hours after the first symptoms and 10 hours after the onset of severe pains in the legs. Aortotomy and arteriotomy on both femorals were done.

Heparin was given during the operation and continuously for the next few days, and the patient recovered. In 1940 Groth (Uppsala) published an account of a case of embolism in the femoral artery, in which, after removal of the embolus, the lumen of the vessels became repeatedly occluded by fibrin coagula. Having reopened the sutures several times in vain, he administered 100 mg. of heparin into the cleansed vessel and treated the patient with smaller doses of heparin during the next few days. The patient recovered. Successful removal of an embolus of $4\,^1/_2$ day's standing in the popliteal artery, performed under heparin, was reported by Lindgren and Wilander in 1941, together with 6 successful embolectomies carried out within 12 hours after the onset of symptoms, 2 thrombectomies on the femoral vein and one vascular suture.

A successful removal of a saddle embolus from the bifurcation of the aorta was reported by Ravdin in 1941. A more comprehensive paper dealing with aortic embolectomies and referring to 5 successful operations of this kind was written by Murray in 1943.

It is difficult to make a definite statement about the scheme of heparin treatment in vascular surgery. Murray recommends continuous infusion, 15—25 drops per minute of Ringer's solution containing 20 ml. of 1 per cent heparin solution (200 mg. of the Toronto heparin) per litre. The coagulation time is kept at about 15 minutes and checked by repeated tests. As Atlas (1942) pointed out, however, many of these patients have cardiac disease so that intravenous saline infusion cannot be given and to them heparin should be administered in single injections, e. g. 50 mg., every four hours.

Lindgren and Wilander gave the heparin in single doses, 0.75 mg. per kilo of body weight, beginning during the operation. After 1 to 2 hours the same dose was repeated. The coagulation time must be repeatedly checked in order to avoid overdosage. Thereafter 1 mg. per kilo of body weight is given every 4 or 6 hours, or the scheme recommended by Crafoord is followed ($50+50+50+100$ mg. a day or possibly $75+75+75+125$ mg.). Thus about 300 mg. a day of a heparin with 80 units per mg. is the daily dose. The heparin is continued until the patient can move about, preferably until he has got up. The amount of heparin given and the number of injections are successively lessened.

In major vascular operations on the heart, the Ductus Botalli and isthmus aortae, the tendency to bleed almost prevents the use of heparin post-operatively. At any rate, the drug should be used cautiously (Crafoord). Instead of the coagulation tendency, which used to limit vascular surgery, we now have to combat the tendency to bleed. Even if there is no immediate relationship between the coagulation time of the blood and the bleeding time from wounds and lesions, there is a risk that haemorrhages may arise in the field of operation. This is particularly the case when heparin has to be given during the operation or shortly after. It is quite possible, however, to perform embolectomies on heparinized patients if due attention is paid to haemostasis. A couple of hours after operation there is, however, as Lindgren and Wilander pointed out, an increased tendency to bleed when the blood pressure returns to its normal level. Furthermore, blood is oozing through the suture canals in the walls of the vessels, which are deficiently thickened with clots if the operation has been performed under treatment with heparin. Thus Lam, in 1941, reported bleeding from a wound in the popliteal space following embolectomy, in two cases as late as four days after operation. The sectioned arteries, however, remained patent. The use of fibrin foam and thrombin superficially lessens or excludes the risk of local oozing of blood in the operation field.

The introduction of heparin has reawakened interest in the question of the treatment of *peripheral arterial embolism*. Excellent results had previously been obtained, very often without operation, by using vasodilators, papaverine and the Pavaex apparatus as introduced by Louis Herrmann. By these means, possibly supplemented by a paravertebral sympathetic injection, the extremities can very often be saved. Now, heparin has come to be a valuable adjunct to this treatment irrespective of whether embolectomy is to be performed or not (Olovson 1939, Rosenqvist 1941, Atlas 1942, Reynolds and Jirka 1944). According to Atlas 0.03 gm. of papaverine hydrochloride and 50 mg. of heparin as advocated by Sedwitz are administered intravenously every four hours, day and night, for the first two days. If improvement follows, the treatment is continued for one week or more, if not, embolectomy is performed.

Papaverine and heparin are given as soon as possible in order to lessen the vasospasm and to counteract thrombus formation round the embolus. Heparin is administered in fairly large doses. If operation is to be performed the heparin can be instantaneously neutralized by the intravenous injection of 5 or 10 ml. of a sterile 1 per cent protamine sulphate solution. At the end of the operation heparin can be given again. The coagulation time of the blood must be carefully controlled and can be regulated at will. Here the use of protamine is very valuable.

The surgical treatment of arterial embolism was most thoroughly discussed by McClure and Harkins in 1942.

Details for arterial embolectomy, the location of the embolus, the operative technique and the treatment with heparin, papaverine, sympathetic novocaine block and continuous intermittent venous occlusion, were given in a paper by Reynolds and Jirka (1944). They gave heparin preoperatively in 6 cases, thereby preventing central growth of the embolus and intravascular clotting during the operation. They did not experience any capillary oozing and consider that heparin should be given in every case as soon as the diagnosis is established. At the end of the operation they gave heparin intravenously, enough to keep the coagulation time at about 15 minutes, usually 50 mg. every four hours. Sympathetic novocaine block may be applied just before the patient leaves the table, and papaverine hydrochloride is given continuously.

A similar description of the technique for arterial embolectomies is given by Duncan and Meyers (1943).

Post-operatively, heparin was given either immediately or within a few hours. Fifty mg. of heparin may be given at the start of an infusion and then enough heparin may be added to the infusion bottle to give the patient approximately 50 mg. every four hours. The coagulation time should be tested by the capillary method every hour and maintained at about fifteen minutes. This infusion may be continued for the first twenty-four hours after which heparin is given in single 50 mg. doses, or thereabouts, every four hours during the day, 100 mg. of heparin being given at night. The administration of heparin is continued for one week and then gradually reduced.

The details of the diagnosis and treatment in embolism of the popliteal artery were given by Doane (1943), who described his results in 11 cases. Particulars were given concerning the post-operative care and the heparin treatment.

CHAPTER VIII

Heparin in Latent Thrombosis, in Pneumonia and Other Inflammatory Conditions.

Venous thrombosis is much more common than is indicated by the clinical signs. When particular attention is paid to this question, the pathologists find thrombosis of the smaller veins of the calf muscles in a surprisingly high number of cases submitted to post-mortem examination. Thus Hunter et. al. (1939) found such changes in not less than 52.7 per cent of the cases and even higher figures are reported. That even advanced thrombosis may easily escape detection is evident from the high percentage of thromboembolisms in which a pulmonary embolism is the first sign of the thrombosis. It is very often the only one.

Thrombosis thus often develops without being detected, particularly in the pelvic veins. The differential diagnosis, when the rise in temperature could be due to the original disease, may be extremely difficult. Because of the great danger involved in this condition a correct diagnosis is desirable.

In obstetric cases with an unexplained pyrexia a few days after parturition, heparin has proved to be effective in depressing the temperature. Heparin treatment was applied as a routine measure in similar cases by B. Lundquist at the Southern Maternity Hospital, Stockholm, and similar experiments with dicumarol were later reported by Lehmann. The rapid disappearance of the fever was very striking and seemed to be connected with the treatment.

Thrombi in the pelvic veins or in the venous plexus surrounding the prostate are not uncommon after operations on the bladder. Because they often give rise to fatal pulmonary embolism they should be borne in mind.

The importance of these latent thrombi has recently been amply demonstrated. It has been found that many *pneumonic processes resistant to sulphonamides or penicillin are very favourably influenced by large doses of heparin or dicumarol*. Kallner and Olsson (1946) reported on similar cases and stated that latent peripheral thrombi should be suspected when sulphonamide therapy fails. The following illustrative cases were described.

Case 1. A married woman, aged 68, fell ill on Oct. 10 with signs of pneumonia. She was given sulphonamide therapy and her temperature dropped to 38.5—39° C. No signs of thrombosis. Dicumarol treatment started on Nov. 9. Prothrombin index on Nov. 10, 26. Sharp pains in the chest suggestive of pulmonary embolism. Heparin treatment was instituted and at the same time the dicumarol therapy was also continued. A rapid drop in temperature and an uneventful recovery followed.

Case 2. Severe uncompensated mitral lesion. Pyrexia up to 40° C. Treated with sulphonamides. Temperature fell, but began to rise again after a few days. Sulphonamides had no effect. Heparin therapy instituted. The temperature rapidly became normal.

Case 3. A man, aged 40, under treatment for ulcerative colitis. Symptoms of colitis since December 1944. A caecal fistula in May 1945. Treated at the Caroline Hospital from Sept. 12, 1945. Afebrile on admission. S. R. 5 mm. Frequent loose mucous stools. Treated with Salazothiazole,[1] sulphapyridine and Salazopyrine.[2] Operation on Dec. 6, closure of the caecal fistula. Subsequently high fever and on Dec. 19, signs of right-sided pleuro-pneumonia. Sulphapyridine treatment, given between Dec. 17 and Dec. 26, had no effect. Penicillin, Dec. 26—Jan. 2, without effect. On the suspicion of deep thrombosis dicumarol therapy was started on Jan. 3, and the temperature dropped to normal the following day. The patient was subsequently afebrile and made a rapid recovery.

The authors were not surprised to find that the number of pneumonias resistant to sulphonamide therapy was considerably reduced when anticoagulant therapy was given simultaneously. On the other hand, fever with an uncertain

---

[1] (4 Thiazil-2-amidosulphanil) 3-carboxy-4-oxyazobenzene.

[2] (4 Pyridyl-2-amidosulphanil) 3-carboxy-4-oxyazobenzene.

aetiology was in many instances found not to have been
due to thrombosis.

*Originally the anticoagulants were given in order to study
their influence upon the pneumonic processes as such.* Because of the accumulation of fibrinogen and its coagulation
during the hepatization of the lungs in pneumonia it seemed
reasonable to suppose that the anticoagulant therapy, although not specific, might have a favourable influence upon
the course of the pneumonia. Experiments along that line
were initiated by Knut Hallberg, Hudiksvall, in 1944.[1]
They were taken up by Wassén and his co-workers, although
from a different aspect.

As shown by Zimmerman and de Takats (1931), the
inflammatory oedema and the perivascular exudate in
thrombophlebitis contain fibrinogen. After coagulation this
provokes an infiltration of fibroblasts and an organization
into dense fibrous tissues. The same occurs in acute rheumatic polyarthritis. To counteract the formation of capillary thrombi and inhibit the deposition of fibrin in the
inflamed tissue, Wassén and Zander (1945) started to treat
cases of acute rheumatic polyarthritis with dicumarol. They
found that the acute periarthritic symptoms were improved
by the treatment. Zander (1946) found that the acute
symptoms in erythema nodosum were influenced by dicumarol treatment. He treated 9 cases. In three of them the
local symptoms, the pain and the pyrexia quickly receded.

Pursuing this idea, Zilliacus (1945) suggested the application of *intense heparin treatment in acute poliomyelitis.*
He thought it possible that the improved circulatory conditions to be expected might facilitate the nutrition of the
ganglia cells. He treated 20 cases, 16 of them in an early
paralytic state. To this series were added 10 more cases
of acute poliomyelitis, treated with heparin by Magnusson
and Lindahl (1945) and submitted to a thorough neuro-
logical examination before and during the course of the
treatment. These authors made the following statement:
"It seems quite natural that an agent which prevents the

---

[1] Personal communication to the author.

formation of fibrin from fibrinogen could also counteract the development of inflammatory symptoms. The effect of heparin and also of dicumarol on the inflammatory symptoms of acute thrombosis of the deep veins is striking. The temperature falls and the symptoms of tissue oedema, pain and swelling subside immediately, the effect being just as obvious as in any other application of specific therapy. Should the oedema and the precipitated fibrin in and around the diseased foci in the spinal cord prevent the passage of fluid and the nutrition of the tissues, then a depression of the coagulative properties of blood ought to have a favourable effect.''

So far the value of this treatment cannot be discussed. The unpredictable course of this disease during the acute stage makes an evaluation difficult. An unduly optimistic view of the treatment might give rise to considerable misuse of the anticoagulants. Although speculatively sound, the treatment with heparin may prove to be of no value in poliomyelitis. Until this question is settled the treatment is not to be recommended.

CHAPTER IX

The Prevention and Treatment of Thrombosis with Dicumarol.

In 1934 when Morawitz summarized the possibilities of influencing thrombosis, he deplored the fact that heparin was so expensive, Germanin so toxic, and hirudin both. He then suggested another approach to the problem. The same result could possibly be obtained if we could find an agent causing a mild, harmless impairment of the liver function, eliminating the prothrombin and fibrinogen production without causing irreparable damage like that in chloroform poisoning.

The haemorrhagic agent causing "sweet clover disease" in cattle fulfils these requirements exactly. In moderate doses it prevents prothrombin production and influences the fibrinogen content of the blood; in excessive doses it causes necrosis of the liver cells. By carefully regulating its effect, it seems to be possible to use it in the way suggested by Morawitz.

The studies of Link et. al. on this haemorrhagic agent, resulting in the identification of it with the synthetic 3.3 methylen-bis-(4 hydroxycoumarin), were performed at a time when the discussion on the coagulation of the blood was at its height owing to the newly discovered possibility of treating thrombo-embolism with heparin. Consequently, this new substance was at once taken up as a therapeutic agent. It was named "dicumarol" by the Council of Pharmacy of the American Medical Association.

After synthetic dicumarol had been made available by Link and Stahmann in September 1940, Bingham, Meyer and Pohle at the Medical Clinic of the University of Wisconsin, Madison, performed experiments on dogs and human beings with a view to ascertaining its mode of action and usefulness. Their observations were published in October 1941.

In tests on dogs the dicumarol was administered by mouth in capsules, and later its sodium salt was given intravenously. Both a single large dose and repeated large and small doses were tried. A single dose of 300 mg. per kg of body weight killed a dog within 15 hours. A dose of 30 mg. per kg., repeated on four consecutive days, as well as a similar dose given three to four times at intervals of a few days, also proved fatal. The reaction to smaller doses was extremely individual, as was to be expected, and the effect on the prothrombin and coagulation times highly variable from animal to animal. Doses of 0.5—50 mg. per kg were given intravenously to 21 dogs. *After doses of more than 35 mg. per kg the animals died within 18 hours from coma, without haemorrhage.* In one case, a single dose of 20 mg. per kg had a fatal outcome due to haemorrhage seven days later.

A similar immediate toxic effect resulting in hyperglyc-aemia, rise in temperature without hypoprothrombinaemia and circulatory collapse with dilatation of the capillaries was found by Wakim and Gatch (1943) and Wakim, Chen and Gatch (1943) after injection of the sodium salt of dicumarol intravenously in dogs, rabbits and rats. A dose of 40 mg. per kilo proved fatal within 30 minutes.

At a meeting of the American Medical Association in May 1942, comprehensive reports of experiments with dicumarol were made by Wright and Prandoni of Columbia University, and by Bollman and Preston, and Allen, Barker and Waugh, of the Mayo Clinic at Rochester. The following is a brief account of their observations.

Dosage. On the first day, 300 mg. in capsules, by mouth, on the second day 200 mg. If the prothrombin time has risen to 30—35 seconds (normal value, 19—20 seconds) on the morning of the third day, that day's dose is not given. The same dosage is continued with a daily control of the prothrombin time. A greater degree of accuracy in the prothrombin time determinations is attained by diluting the

13

plasma with 1, 3, or 6 parts of physiological saline. The latent period of 24—48 hours which elapses before the prothrombin time of 35 seconds is reached is equally long if the sodium salt of the dicumarol is administered intravenously. No stable solutions for intravenous medication were obtainable.

The effect of a given dose is highly variable in different individuals. Unlike heparin, dicumarol does not act directly upon the components of the blood; its action affects instead the prothrombin production in the liver and will consequently vary with the resistance of the liver in different individuals. A dosage system based on the body weight cannot be followed. The dosage must be regulated by the daily prothrombin determinations. Next to the long latent period, the unpredictable effect of the dicumarol treatment is its weakest point. The effect lasts for several days and even up to one week. It can be temporarily discontinued by a blood transfusion and by giving large doses of vitamin K. Wright and Prandoni stated that the blood must be fresh; citrated blood, 4 days old, proved ineffective. As pointed out by Lehmann, large doses of vitamin K, 100—200 mg. given by mouth, effectively reduce the prothrombin time.

In 1945 Jaques and Irish showed that the effect of dicumarol on the liver influences both the production of fibrinogen and the prothrombin synthesis. The lag in the response corresponds to the time necessary for the prothrombin to be used up. Small doses may cause a mild liver injury and stimulate the production of fibrinogen, large doses may cause more severe injury and depress the formation of fibrinogen. Still larger doses give rise to liver cell necrosis. Degenerative liver cell changes and necrosis of the cells under the influence of dicumarol intoxication were also reported by Jansen (1943, 1944).

Dicumarol in the treatment of thrombosis.

As is to be expected, *dicumarol counteracts the formation of thrombi in the blood vessels.* Animal experiments similar to those performed by Murray and Best with heparin have also been conducted with dicumarol. Blood does not clot in the usual manner in glass cannulas inserted in the carotid artery of dogs given dicumarol, 10 mg. per kg the first day and then 5 mg. per kg the following days (Bollman and Preston 1942). The same is the case with glass cells inserted between the carotid artery and the jugular vein and with veins injured by mechanical means (Dale and Jaques 1942).

Extensive clinical trials were soon started to study the value of dicumarol as a prophylactic and therapeutic agent in thrombosis. A wide field of experimentation was opened up. The final development in this field is not yet to be seen, and the results obtained are still under discussion. Only brief notice is therefore given to some of the most important investigations, such as those of Lehmann and his co-workers in Sweden and those at the Mayo Clinic in Rochester.

The possibility of using dicumarol clinically *to prevent thrombosis* has been extensively studied. Lehmann, in Sweden, who has been engaged in the study of this question since 1941, reported in 1943 on 170 cases treated post-operatively with prophylactic doses of dicumarol with only one case of venous thrombosis and one case of mild pulmonary embolism and no deaths. In an equally large series of cases not treated with dicumarol he had, in 1941, 9 cases with thrombosis, among them 5 with pulmonary embolism and 3 deaths. Bruzelius (1945) extended these studies and treated 1,448 cases post-operatively with dicumarol. He started with 250 mg. of the drug and adjusted the following dose according to the prothrombin curve. The post-operative frequency of thrombosis at the clinic as a whole dropped from 2.8 to 1.5 per cent when the dicumarol prophylaxis was in use, and, within the groups of operations selected for treatment, it dropped to one third of the original figure. Thrombo-emoblism occurred in 19 instances, in 3 of them in spite of a satisfactory effect on the prothrombin content. Haemorrhages occurred in 4.4 per cent of the cases.

Barker, Cromer, Hurn and Waugh (1945) reported on 1,000 surgical patients who were given dicumarol post-operatively to prevent venous thrombosis. Only one patient died, an inadequately treated case. Among these patients 379 had suffered from a previous thrombosis or a pulmonary embolism. On 438 of them abdominal hysterectomy was performed. In a previous series from the Mayo Clinic comprising 678 cases with non-fatal pulmonary embolism occurring during the period 1927—1940, subsequent thrombosis had occurred in 43.8 per cent and fatal pulmonary embolism in 8.3 per cent. In this series 180 such cases were treated with dicumarol. Only two of them showed pulmonary embolism and one died. Of 897 patients from the earlier series showing thrombophlebitis 10.6 per cent had subsequent thrombosis and 5.7 per cent a fatal pulmonary embolism. Of 138 similar patients in the latter series given dicumarol, only 4 showed a recurrence of the symptoms and none of them died. A very remarkable fact was that no embolism developed among the 438 patients on whom abdominal hysterectomy had been performed, although a frequency of 4 per cent for post-operative thrombophlebitis and 0.7 per cent for fatal pulmonary embolism was expected in this series. Minor bleeding occurred in 3.9 per cent of the cases and major haemorrhages in 2.5 per cent.

The authors succeeded in keeping the prothrombin level between 30 and 10 per cent of normal as determined by a modification of the Quick method. A water-soluble vitamin K preparation was given intravenously in 37 patients. All of them, except for two, responded satisfactorily to the treatment.

As to the dosage, the 200 mg. dose on the second day may be considered somewhat large, at least in patients who have not previously suffered from thrombo-embolism. In many instances, such as renal or hepatic insufficiency, subacute bacterial endocarditis, or after operations on the brain and the spinal cord, this treatment was considered as contra-indicated.

Without giving any clinical evidence Daughtry (1945) recommended the use of dicumarol in the prophylaxis and treatment of thrombosis. Well aware of its disadvantages he suggested a more cautious administration of it, 200 mg. the first and 100 mg. the second day, starting not earlier than 72 hours after an operation in the case of a prophylactic treatment. Consequently, he stated that often no noticeable change in the prothrombin time appears until 48—72 hours have elapsed after administering the dicumarol. Holmen (1946) recommended 250 mg. on the day after operation. When the prothrombin index begins to rise on the third or fourth day the next dose is given. When the index is depressed below 20 per cent 50—200 mg. of vitamin K are given intravenously.

Without doubt, a very extensive literature will accumulate in the future on this subject. The present author regards these experiments unfavourably. A prophylactic postoperative anticoagulant therapy in all patients seems out of the question. The daily prothrombin determinations make the general use of this treatment impossible. The haemorrhages following the treatment will be more frequent than the thrombo-embolic complications to be expected without the treatment. Serious accidents will also occur. Furthermore, there seems to be little need for this prophylaxis, since an early diagnosis may be made and the incipient thrombosis successfully treated with heparin.

It remains to decide whether heparin or dicumarol, or both in conjunction, should be used in the cases where the risk of thrombosis is evident, e. g. after traumatic lesions or in cases with thrombosis on frequent earlier occasions. Satisfactory evidence of the efficiency of heparin treatment is available, and the risk of complications is very much smaller when heparin is used.

Dicumarol is at present quite commonly used as a *therapeutic agent in thrombo-embolism*. Its therapeutic effect has been amply demonstrated. The fall in temperature and the disappearance of the acute symptoms observed shortly after the use of heparin are also observed when dicumarol is used. Although the two drugs differ in many respects, their anticoagulant effects make them both useful therapeutic agents.

Lehmann (1943) reported on 100 cases of established venous thrombosis and Bruzelius (1945) on 113 cases treated with dicumarol and exercises. In the later series recurrence or progress of the thrombo-embolic process occurred in 23 cases, in 8 of them in spite of a highly depressed prothrombin level. The time spent in bed was shortened from 34—37 days without treatment to 15 days. Haemorrhages occurred in 9.7 per cent of the patients, a higher figure than in the prophylactic series, owing to the higher doses used. In Bruzelius' whole series of 1,656 patients profuse haemorrhage occurred in 13 cases, with two or three deaths.

A total of 180 cases of non-fatal pulmonary embolism treated with dicumarol were reported from the Mayo Clinic in 1945 by Barker, Cromer, Hurn and Waugh. In 1.1 per cent of these cases there were subsequent attacks of thrombosis or non-fatal embolism or infarction. In 0.6 per cent fatal embolism occurred. In the last mentioned cases the attack occurred after the prothrombin value had returned to normal. The corresponding figures for a larger number of similar cases not receiving dicumarol were 43.8, and 18.3 per cent respectively.

Zilliacus (1946) found in his material 131 patients with venous thrombosis in the leg treated with dicumarol and 103 similar patients treated with heparin in conjunction with dicumarol. In these series the effect of the treatment was almost as good as in the heparin series. The patients were kept in bed for 8—11 days and only one death occurred.

Less successful results were reported by Evans (1944). Out of 55 patients treated with dicumarol 8 developed postoperative haemorrhages, sufficient to cause death in two of them, and two others suffered pulmonary embolism during the treatment.

Treatment with heparin and dicumarol.

In 1945 de Takats and Fowler treated 68 cases with heparin and dicumarol. Embolism or spread of the thrombosis occurred in only two of these cases, both of which had been treated with large doses of vitamin K to counteract undue activity of the dicumarol. Attention was drawn to Walker and Rhoad's observation in 1944 that dicumarol increased the sensitivity to heparin.

The effect of heparin in dogs was enhanced by the administration of dicumarol. After an effective dose of dicumarol 50 mg. of heparin was 25—40 per cent more active, as measured by the elevation of the coagulation time. Walker and Rhoads gave for therapeutic purposes 150—200 mg. of the Toronto heparin a day in intravenous drip or divided into 4 intramuscular injections every six hours, together with 300 mg. of dicumarol the first day and 200 mg. the following days until the prothrombin concentration reached 20 per cent.

Dosage of dicumarol.

In the use of dicumarol, no definite dose of the drug can be prescribed because of the unpredictable reaction of the patient. Usually 250 or 300 mg. are given the first day. The second day 200 mg. or even 100 mg. may prove to be too large a dose. Some patients, mainly old people or persons with anaemia, infections, or a bad nutritional condition, show an exceedingly marked reaction with a sudden drop in the prothrombin level or a disappearance of the prothrombin for some time. In case of infections or of an increased atmospheric temperature, there may arise a sudden increase in the patient's susceptibility towards dicumarol (Brambel 1945) with a tendency to intoxication from quite small doses of the drug. In other cases the patients may prove very resistant. In the former cases there is a tendency to bleed, in the latter no therapeutic effect can be achieved. Without daily prothrombin determinations the most serious complications are likely to occur or the therapeutic effect may be absent.

On the other hand, the prothrombin concentration is in many cases said to have been kept at the desired level for a long time.

The most dangerous situation may arise when physicians without knowledge of the physiology of the coagulation of the blood begin to use dicumarol. In Sweden it was not uncommon for two or three tablets a day to be given to patients in their home without any control analyses until

the patients had to be admitted to hospital for haemorrhage. Although only a proportion of these cases were reported, a considerable number of cases have been published
in the Swedish medical press.

Shlevin and Lederer (1944) reported a fatal case of dicumarol treatment for retinal vein thrombosis in which
100 mg. of dicumarol had been given daily for three weeks
without any prothrombin determinations. The patient died
on the 18th day after the end of the treatment.

The technique of *the prothrombin determinations* to be applied
in clinical practice has been described by Quick in his recent
monograph (1942). Numerous modifications of his method have
been suggested by different authors. The technique has also been
simplified by leaving out the citrate and the recalcification, taking
the blood with a pipette directly from the ear into a kinase
solution at 37° C. (Holmen 1946.)

Summary.

Experience in using dicumarol so far indicates that it
has a marked specific therapeutic effect in thrombosis. The
easy availability and the prolonged effect facilitates its use.
In practice, however, the necessity of making daily prothrombin determinations limits its use to hospitals with
laboratory facilities. Furthermore, dicumarol is ineffective
in checking the further growth of an early thrombosis. It
is repeatedly observed that a phlegmasia alba dolens develops from a venous thrombosis in the calf when only dicumarol and active movements are given. Likewise, it is of no
use in massive pulmonary embolism.

Unfortunately, dicumarol is far from an ideal remedy for
thrombosis. The impairment of the liver function is a very
serious disadvantage. It is, namely, practically impossible
to make a distinction between the therapeutic and the toxic
effect. Large doses are known to cause liver cell necrosis.
The action of dicumarol is a kind of toxic narcosis of the
liver cells, the depth of which is difficult to control.

CHAPTER X

Some Aspects of the Pathogenesis of Thrombosis and of its Treatment.

It is beyond the scope of this monograph to enter into a detailed discussion of the different aspects of the pathogenesis of thrombosis, its clinical symptoms and the different prophylactic and therapeutic measures suggested by various authors. They are dealt with only in so far as they actually have some connection with the early diagnosis of thrombosis and the specific treatment with anticoagulants. Further details are to be found in the inaugural dissertations of Hellsten (1942) and of Zilliacus (1946) and in the summarizing papers of Ochsner (1945) and of de Takats and Fowler (1945).

The Sites of Predilection of Deep Venous Thrombosis.

It is very fortunate that thrombosis as a rule begins in the distal parts of the lower extremities. Here an early diagnosis can easily be made and, with appropriate treatment, the process can be checked and the growth of the thrombosis can be limited to a peripheral area. Our knowledge of the early stages of thrombosis was, however, until quite recently very unsatisfactory. Virchow's original conception was accepted for almost a century. After his discovery in 1846, that pulmonary embolism follows thrombosis of the femoral and pelvic veins, these venous areas were taken to be sites of predilection for deep venous thrombosis. Recently a different view has been accepted, based on morbid anatomy and clinical findings.

In 1929 Denecke found at autopsies the deep plantar veins of the foot thrombosed in both diagnosed and undiagnosed thrombosis in 2 out of 22 normal feet and in all the seven cases of femoral vein thrombosis anlyzed by him. Hence he drew the conclusion that thrombosis not infrequently begins in the plantar veins and recommended routine examination of the sole of the foot when thrombosis was suspected. "It would be very valuable if the tenderness found on palpation of the plantar region in the future should prove to be a reliable sign of thrombosis, allowing us at least in a number of cases to make an early diagnosis at a time when the extension of the thrombosis to the calf and thigh possibly could be prevented by elevating the leg, medical gymnastics or by other means." The present coincidence of effective therapy and the understanding of the importance of plantar venous thrombosis makes Denecke's conclusions classical.

Frykholm (1940) made a survey of the much quoted works of the German authors, Rössle and Neumann, as well as of his own experience. Hunter et. al. (1945) summarizing the recent literature, mentioned that Homans, supported by clinical observations and post-mortem material, had emphasized as early as 1934 the great importance of the veins of the calf as the origin of ascending thrombi.

At 324 autopsies where the calf veins were examined Rössle (1937) found thrombosis in the leg in 88 cases, the process being limited to the calf veins in 50 cases (62 per cent). In 38 cases the veins of both the calf and the thigh were thrombosed and in only 7 cases femoral thrombosis alone was present.

In 1938, Neumann examined 100 cases of thrombosis of the leg post mortem. The plantar veins were involved in 71 cases, the calf veins in 87 cases and the veins of the thigh in 22 cases. Solitary plantar vein thrombosis occurred in 11 per cent and solitary calf vein thrombosis in 24 per cent of the cases. There was no case with the thrombosis limited to the femoral veins.

Frykholm (1939, 1940) analyzed 24 cases of thrombosis post mortem. In 18 cases the thrombosis of the leg was

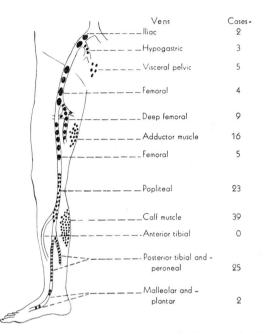

Vens	Cases・
Iliac	2
Hypogastric	3
Visceral pelvic	5
Femoral	4
Deep femoral	9
Adductor muscle	16
Femoral	5
Popliteal	23
Calf muscle	39
Anterior tibial	0
Posterior tibial and peroneal	25
Malleolar and plantar	2

Fig. 21. Sites of venous thrombosis with number of cases for different veins of lower leg as found by Frykholm (1940) at post mortem examination of 24 cases.

bilateral, thus giving a total of 42 extremities to be analyzed. The sites of the thrombi are illustrated in Fig. 21.

Frykholm was the first to point out the importance of venous thrombosis in the adductor region, and he laid particular stress upon its diagnosis. It occurred not less than 16 times in 42 extremities with thrombosis.

Thrombi in the veins of the calf have repeatedly been found in a very high percentage of post-mortem examinations. Rössle (1937) found in his 324 autopsies on adults similar changes in 25 per cent of the cases, Putzer (1939) in 27 per cent of 370 autopsies. Hunter et. al. (1941) found in 351 autopsies the incidence of thrombosis in the deep veins of the leg to be as high as 52.7 per cent among middle-aged and older persons forced to stay in bed for varying periods of time. In 110 cases bilateral involvement was found. The authors considered that when thrombosis occurs in the legs it is likely to be bilateral. The clots were much more frequent in and along the soleus muscle than in the gastrocnemius.

Although Allen, Linton and Donaldson (1945) state that in 95 per cent of the cases with pulmonary embolism diagnosed post mortem, the emboli originated in the deep veins of the leg and Bauer (1946) holds a similar view, the fact must not be forgotten that thrombosis in the pelvic and iliac veins is still quite common in obstetric-gynaecological clinics and after operations on the bladder. The difficulty of making an early diagnosis renders this field still more important. In fact, anticoagulants, heparin or dicumarol, are given in similar undefined cases as a diagnostic aid, conclusions being drawn *ex juvantibus*. In case of a thrombosis in the pelvic veins there is an immediate drop in the temperature and an alleviation of the symptoms on the administration of heparin.

Ætiology of Thrombosis.

Venous stasis, injuries to the intima of the blood vessels and chemical changes in the composition of the blood are considered to be the main aetiological factors causing thrombosis of the veins.

Venous stasis is certainly the most important. Thrombosis and pulmonary embolism almost exclusively occur in bedridden, mostly elderly, persons, where the influence of the muscular work on the venous circulation is absent. Exercises and early ambulation of the patients reduce the incidence of post-operative thrombosis.

By means of phlebography, Frimann-Dahl (1935) demonstrated that there is a pronounced retardation of venous blood flow in the legs after operations known to have a high frequency of post-operative thrombosis. It may become so pronounced that the blood in the veins almost comes to a standstill. Usually the veins empty in 10—30 seconds. After operations, the emptying is delayed by 2 to 4 minutes. The retardation begins on the second day after operation and has a tendency to last during the whole time the patient stays in bed.

Potts and Smith (1941) demonstrated experimentally in dogs that simultaneous elevation of both hind legs increased the flow of blood through the vena cava by 100 to 150 per cent. Simultaneously, artificial hyperventilation produced a further increase in the rate of circulation. The extremely high frequency of thrombosis after trauma to the lower leg is probably a result of impaired circulation, but might also partly be due to vascular lesions.

Hunter et. al. (1939) made a study of the influence of exercises and early ambulation on the incidence of thrombosis. Since they considered that the confinement to bed was the most important aetiological factor favouring thrombus formation in the lower extremity, they studied the incidence of thrombosis in the veins of the calf at post-mortem examinations of two series of patients. In the first series with 130 autopsies, the treatment had been conservative; in the second one with 39 autopsies, voluntary exercises under supervision and early ambulation had been applied. In the first series thromboses in the veins of the calf were found in 53 per cent of the bodies and in the second series in only 18 per cent, showing a decrease of 35 per cent.

The importance of the mechanical factor is strikingly demonstrated in the condition described as "shelter leg" by Simpson (1940). Elderly persons sitting during the "Blitz" in London for long periods of time in chairs with wooden crossbars causing pressure on the back of the thigh or on the popliteal vessels often developed thrombosis of the leg, followed by death from pulmonary embolism.

The non-inflammatory nature of thrombosis is the most probable in the majority of cases. Thus Hunter et. al. (1939), on histological examination, found signs of a phlebitic infection in only 5.9 and 2.5 per cent in two series of autopsies, with 200 cases in each series, and non-infective phlebothrombosis in the veins of the leg in not less than 59 and 44 per cent. Similarly, Murray and MacKenzie (1942) found no evidence of an inflammatory origin in most of the deep venous thrombi. The specific therapeutic effect of the anticoagulants was also considered by them to indicate the primary importance of disorders of the clotting mechanism.

The recent application of anticoagulants in the treatment of thrombosis has further substantiated this view about the aetiology of venous thrombosis. The immediate fall in temperature and the alleviation of the local symptoms clearly indicate the specific nature of the treatment. *Consequently, anticoagulants, active movements and early ambulation must be the treatment of choice in thrombosis and pulmonary embolism.*

The Influence of Medical Gymnastics and Early Ambulation on the Frequency of Thrombo-Embolism.

Movements, active or passive, and early ambulation were the most successful of the early means for reducing the incidence of thrombo-embolism. Gauss's statement "Pessimum remedium quies" expresses the underlying principle most clearly (Gauss 1934).

A system with deep breathing and active movements in bed, possibly supported by special equipments such as Payr's (1930) foot roller and Gamble's (1935) bicycle pedals, was developed (see Parson 1945).

As early as 1925 Hermansson reported that intensive exercises caused a 50 per cent reduction in thrombo-embolic complications after gynaecological operations. The earlier literature on this subject is to be found in papers by Jaschke (1937), Potts (1940), Campeanu (1941) and Backer-Gröndahl (1944). Reference is also made to a recent monograph by Ochsner (1945, p. 252) and particularly to a summarizing paper of Newburger (1943). One of the most enthusiastic supporters of early ambulation, Campeanu showed convincingly that it is not accompanied by any discomfort. Thus in 20,090 patients who got out of bed within 24 hours of the operation, 6,508 of them directly from the operation table, there were no complications such as suture ruptures to be seen, nor were there any phlebitic symptoms.

Recent papers deal more thoroughly with this subject (Ham 1944, Potts 1943). The last-mentioned author reported 837 consecutive major operations without any post-operative thromboses. According to Allen, Linton and Donaldson (1945), prior to 1925 3 patients out of each thousand subjected to major surgical procedures succumbed to pulmonary embolism. Since that time active and passive movements and early ambulation had reduced the figure to approximately one per thousand. Evans (1944) reported that the frequency of pulmonary embolism in a surgical clinic where bicycle exercises were most faithfully carried out during a winter season was only a third of that in a neighbouring hospital where no particular measures were taken.

The opinion is now quite commonly held that early ambulation has many advantages as a method of post-operative treatment. Besides the reduction in the number of the post-operative complications from the lungs and the thromboembolic processes, the physical and mental condition of the patient is very favourably influenced by the early ambulation. The stay in hospital is shortened. Many more patients can be treated in a ward, and the expense to the patient or the community is reduced.

When these principles are applied on a larger scale the incidence of thrombosis and pulmonary embolism is reduced to a half or a third of the previous figures. This is evident from a comparison of Tables XXVII and XXVIII which express the frequency of thrombosis from the times before (Table XXVII) and after (Table XXVIII) the introduction of the exercises in bed and the early ambulation of the patients.

Although these prophylactic measures exert a decisive influence on the incidence of thrombo-embolic complications, they nevertheless do not make therapeutic measures in thrombosis unnecessary. Despite the claims of some enthusiastic supporters early ambulation does not give complete protection against thrombo-embolic complications, not even if started on the first or second day (D'Ingiami 1945). At best, the incidence of thrombosis in surgical cases is still about 0.6 per cent. Without specific treatment the mortality among these cases of thrombosis is still above 20 per cent (Table XXVIII). In the medical clinics where movement therapy is more or less inapplicable similar figures are found.

When Morawitz (1934) doubted whether it was possible to eliminate thrombo-embolic complications by non-specific means he said:

"All our means for the prevention of thrombosis seem to me to be of a very limited value. Real progress in this field is not to be expected unless we are able to influence not only the mechanical factors but also the fundamental properties of the blood and the blood vessels which induce coagulation and thrombosis."

The Treatment of Thrombosis by Free Movement.

Although the value of free movement after operations is widely admitted, the same cannot be said of the application of this principle in the treatment of thrombosis. At first the acute thrombosis, the swelling, tenderness and pain made the patient unwilling to move his legs, and furthermore, attacks of fatal pulmonary embolism were repeatedly observed after movements. Many authors therefore, adopted a totally different line of treatment as soon as a thrombosis was established. Although convinced of the value of exercise in promoting circulation of the blood, Morawitz, in 1934, declared that he, "belehrt durch manche Rückschläge", could not take the responsibility for letting the patient with a thrombosis get up. Consequently, the patients were kept in bed as immobile as possible for weeks and months and for at least two weeks after the acute symptoms had receded. The spread of the process to the other leg in about every third case, the development of a phlegmasia alba dolens, and the occurrence of repeated attacks of pulmonary embolism completed the picture of a terrifying disease. The care of the patients was a real burden for the hospital attendants. Unfortunately, this has been the picture of the thrombo-embolic disease which has prevailed in most countries until recently, as is shown in Scandinavia, for example, in the studies of Linde (1941 a and b, 1944), Hellsten (1942), Zilliacus (1946) and those of the present author (1946 a, b and c). A series of cases from a maternity hospital (Hellsten, 1942) provides a good illustration. Four hundred and sixty-two cases of deep thrombosis were treated during the years 1930—39. The mean duration of pyrexia and hospital in-patient treatment were 34 and 52 days respectively. Twenty-seven patients (5.8 per cent) died of thrombo-embolism.

All kinds of treatments for thrombosis were applied by different authors, but most of them without success (see Hellsten 1942, p. 64). The most promising ones included exercises and early ambulation (Barker and Counseller 1939, Fischer 1940) after application of an elastic bandage (Oehler 1927) or of zink plaster stockings tightly around the leg (Bahls 1940). The only good results have been achieved by two recently introduced methods, by sympathetic block with novocaine and particularly by venous interruption, to be described later on.

Evidently, free mobility and early ambulation starting from the first to third day after operation consistently applied to all the patients in a clinic is likely to shorten the course of thrombosis. Thus Fabricius-Møller and Sørensen had between 1931—1945 114 cases with thrombosis (0.83 per cent) of 13,683 cases operated upon and 33 cases (0.36 per cent) of 9,236 cases not submitted to operation. Among these 147 cases of thrombosis, 52 had only thrombi in the veins of the leg and 77 only pulmonary infarctions; 18 had both. They were kept in bed only 5 to 15 days. Amongst the 147 cases of thrombosis 7 deaths occurred (4.8 per cent), a low mortality, but there were also in their series 33 cases of sudden fatal pulmonary embolism, giving a normal mortality rate, 0.17 per cent among the 22,919 patients. (See Table XXVII.) With anticoagulant therapy,

14

the 7 cases which ended fatally ought also to have been saved.

The general impression is that movement therapy alone is not sufficient, even when persistently and carefully applied. It seems reasonable to assume that our predecessors in medicine would have detected the value of such a simple therapeutic measure as free movements and early ambulation, available since Hippocrates' days, if it *per se* had been sufficient.

The mortality in thrombosis nevertheless remained the same, namely, 19.2 per cent in Germany during the early decades of this century, and 20.6 per cent for the most recent period at the Mayo Clinic in the United States, a clear demonstration that in general thrombosis and pulmonary embolism were uninfluenced by any treatment, as was stated by Morawitz in 1934.

On the same occasion Nürnberger (1934) expressed a still more pessimistic view as to the value of the methods applied in the treatment of thrombosis. Unger considered all procedures applied up to 1938 quite worthless.

Sympathetic Novocaine Block.

In 1934 Leriche and Kunlin reported on three post-operative thrombophlebitic cases treated by novocaine block of the lumbar sympathetic ganglion. This treatment has since that time been fully developed and extensively applied by Leriche himself (1938), by Ochsner and de Bakey, Homans and many others. Thus Ochsner and de Bakey (1939), describing the technique of the sympathetic block, mention twelve authors using the method in thrombophlebitic cases in 1938.

The sympathetic nervous block breaks the vasomotor reflex-arcs and prevents the extensive spasm in the veins and arteries of the affected leg. The clinical manifestations such as pain and swelling due to oedema in the connective tissue are relieved. Uniformly successful results are said to be obtained in every case. According to Ochsner and de Bakey, the temperature falls within 24 hours and is normal within 72 to 96 hours, the swelling begins to decrease and has disappeared within a week. The oedema is considered to be a result of tissue anoxia caused by the arteriospasm (Zimmermann and de Takats 1931). In over one-half of the cases the extremity has returned to its normal size within four days. Rarely more than three injections are necessary.

The technique of the novocaine block was also described by Bancroft (1945). As only temporary relief is obtained with this procedure without any satisfactory protection against pulmonary embolism, Bancroft recommended venous ligation, with thrombectomy, if possible, as a more reliable procedure.

Surgical Treatment of Thrombosis of the Deep Veins of the Lower Extremities.

Proximal venous ligation, possibly in conjunction with removal of the thrombus, has been extensively applied in the United States during the last few years.

This method was originally applied in case of purulent superficial thrombophlebitis. The earlier history of vein interruption, possibly combined with resection of the venous trunk, has been reviewed by Ochsner (1945, p. 256) and by Buxton, Farris, Moyer and Coller (1944). A similar operation to prevent the discharge of an embolus in ordinary thrombophlebitis was performed in the United States by Homans in 1934 (see also Homans 1941).

The operation has recently developed into a general method of treating thrombophlebitis in the deep veins of the leg. Several papers dealing with this subject have appeared. The value attached in certain circles to venous ligation with thrombectomy is evident from Bancroft's statement (1945) that more lives could be saved by this means than by the use of anticoagulants alone.

In June 1944, Allen, Linton and Donaldson (1945), who had performed venous interruption on 464 patients, gave a detailed analysis of 367 cases. Fine and Starr (1945) con-

cluded that "the surgical prophylaxis of pulmonary embolism
is the procedure of choice among those who prefer a more
direct and immediately applicable method for blocking the
discharge of an embolus". Some authors consider it advisable to perform venous ligation in almost all cases with
deep venous thrombosis of the leg, particularly in the non-
inflammatory type with its fresh, friable and non-adherent
clot in the larger veins. Fine and Starr consider that not
even the presence of acute phlebitic symptoms, indicating
a fixation of the thrombus to the wall of the vein, offers
any guarantee that the thrombosis will not spread proximally. They found the practice of ligation on both sides,
irrespective of the apparent extent of the involvement of
either side, to be the safest way of preventing embolism.

Consequently, bilateral femoral vein ligation or ligation of
the iliac veins or even the inferior vena cava is often prac-
tised. Thrombectomy is performed, if necessary by suction
through a glass cannula introduced proximally in the femoral
or iliac vein. The results are in general reported as being
excellent.

The acute symptoms disappear within a few days, the
temperature becoming normal within 5—6 days. Particularly after thrombectomy the local swelling and pain are
quickly relieved. According to Allen, patients who used to
remain in bed for six weeks with a thrombophlebitis would
often be able to leave the hospital within a week. The late
sequelae of post-phlebitic phlegmon is reduced to a mini-
mum if the vein is ligated relatively early.

The details as to the surgical procedure are to be found in
papers by Homans (1944), Fine and Starr (1935), and
Allen, Linton and Donaldson (1945). The operations on
the vessels were, as a routine measure, followed by early
ambulation.

The exploration of the femoral vein and removal of the
clot by suction presents no surgical hazards and can be
quickly carried out even on very ill patients (Parson 1945).
On the other hand, Allen, Linton and Donaldson claim that
oedema may develop after ligation of the common femoral

vein. Ligation is usually made below the saphenous-femoral junction.

New attacks of pulmonary embolism due to thrombosis at the site of the vein ligation are rare. Allen et. al., however, considered heparin to be indicated particularly if suction had been applied and remnants of the thrombus might have been left proximal to the ligature.

Veal and Hussey (1945), who made 98 ligations on 84 patients, ligated the vein above the level of the thrombus just distal to the main tributary. The thrombus was, therefore, trapped below the ligation and the tributary assured an adequate flow of blood, excluding any blind end of vein. The femoral vein was ligated in 51 patients, in 6 of them on both sides. It was necessary to ligate the inferior vena cava in not less than six cases. There were several recurrences of pulmonary embolisms. Of 39 patients with pulmonary embolism before ligation, 9 had a recurrence of the embolism after ligation, in 5 of them originating from the other leg. In three of the remaining cases there was an inflammation above the point of ligation, and in three cases an arterial spasm developed after the venous interruption. In 7 cases death followed, in 4 of them from pre-operative multiple pulmonary embolism and in 3 from recurrent pulmonary embolism originating from the other leg.

In spite of the excellent functional results and the abolition of pain and vasospasm reported by Veal and Hussey to follow ligation, their series of 84 cases with 7 deaths, which occurred in spite of repeated surgical operations, including ligation of the inferior vena cava in 6 cases, clearly demonstrates that this therapy is inferior to the treatment with anticoagulants and active exercises. There is no question about its inferiority. It is another matter, however, to decide to what extent a venous ligation might have been desirable in some of the cases in conjunction with the immediate administration of heparin in large doses.

Evans (1944) did not believe that venous section and ligation was the ultimate answer to the problem of pulmonary embolism. He advocated the use of anticoagulants as an adjunct to ligation when the latter could be considered necessary. At first he had used heparin only, then combined heparin and dicumarol therapy.

Coller (1945) also stressed that further trials with the method of venous ligation are necessary before it can be definitely decided which treatment — surgical or with specific anticoagulants — is the most effective in preventing pulmonary embolism. Similarly, de Takats and Fowler (1945), who had ligated the femoral vein in 39 cases, considered shortly afterwards that many of these ligations were completely unnecessary.

In conjunction with ligation of the veins de Takats and Fowler recommended lumbar sympathetic block to lessen the acute ischaemia and the oedema following it. Veal and Hussey considered also that the circulation, after being improved by the sympathetic block, helps to prevent growth of the thrombus.

The pains after ligation of the femoral vein are in some cases said to be more severe than those following thrombosis of the vein. Severe oedema has also occurred. In one case (Dennis 1945) the ischaemic symptoms caused by the oedema had to be treated by fasciotomy in the thigh and calf.

Venous ligation or anticoagulant therapy in thrombosis of the leg?

The relative merits of anticoagulant therapy and ligation at different stages during the course of a thrombosis will certainly arouse discussion.

Irrespective, however, of the possible future use of anticoagulants, venous ligation seems to be indicated in a certain number of severe cases with suppurative thrombophlebitis in the superficial veins of the lower extremities or in the pelvic veins. Particularly in cases of suppurative pelvic thrombophlebitis, the ligation of both iliac veins or of the vena cava inferior may prove imperative (Ochsner and de Bakey 1943). Here the operation can be life-saving (Buxton, Farris, Mayer and Coller 1944).

There is, however, a tremendous difference between the suppurative pelvic thrombophlebitis and the ordinary venous thrombosis in the leg. In the former there is a serious infection giving rise to bacteriaemia and septic emboli contra-indicating heparinization (Simon 1943). The thrombosis of the veins is here a natural healing process which prevents the spread of new septic emboli. Venous ligation cuts off the infected area from the circulation. In ordinary thrombosis in the leg the clinical picture is quite different. The non-infectious nature is evident in most of the cases. When the secondary inflammatory reaction develops in and around the vein, causing swelling and pains, there is not the same need of preventive venous ligation, because the thrombosis is already fixed to the vascular wall.

It is therefore questionable whether venous ligation is the appropriate treatment in the earliest stage of a thrombosis, instead of anticoagulants which prevent further growth of the clot. It must also be questioned whether venous interruption in the other leg is justified. Even in case of phlegmasia alba dolens, heparinization prevents the spread to the other leg (Zilliacus 1946). Without anticoagulant therapy this complication occurs in every third case with thrombosis in the deep veins of the leg.

In the first place ligation of a larger vein or excision of a part of it is a highly unphysiological procedure. Secondly, the venous return from the leg will be more or less severely impaired, particularly if the common femoral vein has been ligated.

Anticoagulant therapy, routinely performed at a sufficiently early stage, can hardly be replaced by other forms of treatment. Even in severe acute cases treated with anticoagulants there are surprisingly few complications. Heparin can furthermore be applied everywhere outside the surgical clinics without any daily analyses of the blood, and the time of treatment is no longer than the post-operative stay in hospital after a venous ligation.

The experience gained in the Swedish clinics in using heparin or heparin in conjunction with dicumarol seems to make venous ligation superfluous in most cases, with the possible exception of septic thrombophlebitis in the superficial or the pelvic veins, where venous interruption followed by heparin treatment may be indicated. The whole question of the surgical treatment of thrombosis should be reinvestigated against this background. It is possible that venous interruption on a larger scale may in the future prove as unnecessary as the Trendelenburg operation for pulmonary embolism. The surgical interest at one time directed to this operation was out of all proportion to the results of the operative activity. According to Nürnberger (1934), out of the 122 patients operated upon during the period 1908 to 1934, only nine were alive several years after the operation.

Future experience will within a few years show to what extent similar operative procedures on the femoral or iliac veins are justified. Here, as in the Trendelenburg operation, particular stress must be laid on the final result of the treatment, i. e. on the sequelae which develop during the years following the acute thrombo-embolic processes.

The Prevention and Treatment of Thrombosis.

The first step in the reduction of the incidence of thrombosis and fatal pulmonary embolism is to educate the medical staff. Interns, private practitioners, nurses, and students must be taught the earliest signs and symptoms of thrombosis and pulmonary embolism. The importance of active exercises and deep breathing regularly performed by bedridden patients, particularly after operations and childbirth, must be emphasized. In fact, this is a problem of re-educating physicians and nurses. Once this object is attained, the clinical picture of this disease will be completely changed.

To this end, one member of the staff at each clinical unit or at every hospital must familiarize himself with this problem, particularly with the technique of administering heparin and dicumarol, with phlebography and with blood analysis. Under his supervision the cases of thrombosis in the wards can then receive appropriate treatment.

It is astonishing how little attention is paid at present to the early diagnosis of thrombosis, although the initial signs of thrombosis are dealt with extensively in textbooks and summarizing papers. Consequently, the number of sudden fatal pulmonary embolisms is large.

Early diagnosis.

An unexplained, intermittent low fever and an increase in pulse rate are vital warning signs. However, according to Veal and Hussey (1945) they are not always present. These authors found fever and tachycardia in only 21 per cent of 84 cases of early venous thrombosis. Local symptoms, swelling and discoloration were present in almost every case. Oedema occurred in 90 per cent, calf tenderness in 96 per cent and Homan's sign — tenderness in the calf or in the popliteal fossa on forcible dorsiflexion of the foot with the leg extended — in 92 per cent. In 61 of their 84 cases there was a sharp, persistent and well localized pain in the calf.

Usually the patients have an aching or burning feeling in the calf or in the thigh, especially at night, which they will acknowledge if questioned.

The most common sign of all is tenderness in the calf on deep palpation. Bauer (1946 a), Hellsten (1942) and Frykholm (1940) gave detailed descriptions of the technique of deep palpation of the calf, recommending a supine position of the patient with both knees raised and the sole of the foot resting on the bed. The relaxed muscles, including those in the adductor region, are palpated with both hands. Induration in the muscles and pain on pressure against the tibia are sought. Homan's sign is nearly always found. Other authors found tenderness in the calf muscles in two-thirds of all their cases and Homan's sign in only 41 per cent. Deep palpation of the sole of the foot is performed as a routine measure because very often thrombosis begins in the plantar veins. Conclusive evidence is obtained by phlebography.

In not less than 38 per cent of their cases Allen et. al.

(1945) found that chest symptoms appeared first, even when the thrombosis began in the lower extremity. This fact is not fully recognized at present. Careful attention is usually paid to the physical examination of the lungs, to the X-ray and the bacteriological examination of the sputum without any suspicion that the "pneumonia" can be an infarction from an embolus. The same attention should be paid to the examination of the legs if possible also by means of phlebography, even in case of mild symptoms from the chest such as sudden pain with breathlessness.

The symptoms from the lungs are particularly important in obstetric and gynaecological cases and after operations on the bladder or the prostate. They are often the first signs indicating a thrombosis in the pelvic veins. In these particular cases, the administration of heparin or possibly of dicumarol very soon gives an indication of the presence or absence of a thrombus.

Phlebography.

Phlebography is a great help in the diagnosis of difficult cases.

The history of the technique of visualizing the veins with X-rays and contrast media was discussed by Hellsten (1942). The first diagnosis by means of this technique was made by Frimann-Dahl (1935), who, during his studies of the venous blood flow in the legs after operations, found a venous thrombosis in two of his cases. Dos Santos (1938) made a comprehensive study of the technique of phlebography. Bauer (1940, 1941 b) was the first to elaborate a routine technique for clinical use. Hellsten (1942) applied this technique in verifying the diagnosis in the first 100 cases of thrombosis treated with heparin by himself. It was soon applied on a larger scale and recommended by different authors (Doughtery and Homans 1940, Welch, Faxon and McGahey 1942, Fine and Sears 1941, Starr, Frank and Fine 1942, Sedwitz 1942, Baker and Sedwitz 1943, and Sedwitz and Baker 1944). It proved to be useful in studying the venous return in all kinds of diseased conditions, such as varicose veins, traumatic lesions, thrombosis in the leg and its sequelae. The phlebographic technique is described by Bauer (1945).

In the diagnosis of early thrombosis of the veins of the calf phlebography gives extremely valuable information. Not only the presence but also the absence of an initial thrombosis can be demonstrated. Thus Bauer found the deep veins of the calf to be patent in 30 per cent of the cases showing initial signs suggestive of a thrombosis. The same percentage was found by Hellsten (1942).

Similarly, phlebographic examination of the legs in cases with pulmonary symptoms of uncertain aetiology is of the utmost value in revealing thrombosis in the calf, which could not be detected clinically.

Heparin therapy.

As soon as the diagnosis of thrombosis has been made, 120—150 mg. of heparin (12,000 units) are administered immediately to a patient of ordinary weight, preferably in the patient's home before he is sent to the hospital. Depending on the time of day at which the diagnosis is made, a further one or two doses of the same amount are given at four hour intervals. The last dose is given late at night. The following days, four injections, each of 100 mg. (8,000 units) are given, the last evening dose preferably being increased to 150 mg. After a few days the temperature returns to normal (or to a level only a few tenths of a degree, Centigrade, above normal), and the swelling and tenderness in the leg disappear. The heparin treatment lasts 5 to 8 days. The ordinary daily dose of heparin at the beginning is 400—500 mg. (150+75+75+150 or 125+100+100+125 mg.), later about 250—350 mg. (125+100+125 mg.) and finally somewhat less. The mean total amount of heparin necessary for a case was in Bauer's series 1.6 gm., in Hellsten's series 2.75 gm., and in Liavaag's and Nicolaysen's series 2.35 gm. The latter figures are more likely to be effective, at least in late cases. All these figures refer to a heparin with 80 provisional international units per mg.

In case of *pulmonary embolism* the same scheme is applied. In severe cases immediate simultaneous heparin and eupaverine treatment is an urgent necessity. Heparin is given in large doses the first day, either 150 mg. every sixth hour or possibly 100 mg. every fourth hour. The risk of sanguineous exudates in the pleural cavity from pulmonary infarctions is very small.

During the entire treatment the patient is allowed to move about freely in bed and is made at intervals to do whole series of deep breathing exercises and bending and stretching movements of the legs throughout the day. On the day the heparin dose is first reduced, he is allowed to get up and even to walk about a little. The length of time out of bed is increased each day, and as a rule the patient can leave the hospital two or three days after getting up.

It is of the utmost importance that the heparin should be given as long as the patient stays in bed. The heparin or dicumarol treatment should not be terminated until the patient has been up and free from fever for at least one day. Practically all the failures experienced in the Swedish series with heparin treatment have occurred in patients who, for one reason or another, stayed in bed for some time after the end of the heparin treatment.

When he first gets up, he is provided with an elastic bandage for his foot and the lower leg in order to prevent the swelling generally noticed in the evening during the first few weeks.

Heparin can also be administered by the continuous drip method, which, however, to a certain extent limits the free mobility of the patient. The infusion method is inapplicable in renal or cardiac disorders. The technique of infusion is described by Priestley and Barker, 1942.

In this discussion very little stress has been laid on *the determination of the coagulation time of the blood.* In the continuous infusion method the coagulation time is checked every three or four hours. In the Swedish series the effect of the heparin has been followed in very few cases. It has, however, been found desirable to determine the coagulation time at least before giving a new dose of heparin to elderly people with impaired renal function. Otherwise an accumulation of heparin in the blood may occur.

If dicumarol is to be administered the first doses, 200 mg. the first day and 100 mg. the second day, are given irrespective of the heparin treatment. The heparin is not withdrawn until a low prothrombin level is reached. Since it is of vital importance, e. g. in acute thrombosis of the deep veins of the calf, that the growth of the thrombus should be checked and its further progression to the popliteal and deep femoral vein prevented, heparin cannot be replaced by dicumarol with its slow action. Only heparin will reliably prevent the extension and growth of the thrombus.

CHAPTER XI

The Social Aspects of Thrombosis.

The Mortality of Pulmonary Embolism after Surgical Operations.

The literature on this subject is very comprehensive. It has been surveyed by several workers, some of whom submit similar figures for the mortality rate, although there is a good deal of variation in different statistics. The following figures are taken from Hellsten's survey of 1942.

Hübner and Freudenberg, in 1941, assembled the material from one hundred surgical and gynaecological clinics in Germany for the period 1919 to 1929. In 532,000 surgical operations there were 1,124, or 0.21 per cent, cases of fatal pulmonary embolism. The very same figure, 0.21 per cent, was obtained by Ranzi and Huber in 1935 in an analysis of 28 statistical series on 492,104 operations. In 1931 Hosoi made a survey of the following series: Cutler and Morton (1917), Hampton and Wharton (1920), Eisenreich (1920), Rupp (1921), Cutler and Hunt (1922), De Quervain (1925), Naegeli (1925), Farr and Spiegel (1929), Fuller (1930), Killian (1930), Geissendörfer (1930) and Hosoi, comprising altogether 225,680 surgical operations, with 578 cases, or 0.256 per cent, of fatal pulmonary embolism. In 1936 Collins reviewed fifteen series of cases, including those of De Quervain with 76,799 operations and of Naegeli with 15,543, and found 785 cases of fatal pulmonary embolism or 0.28 per cent in 282,837 operations. Finally Robertson, in 1938, collected from the entire surgical literature between 1913 and 1931 a series of 2,196,841 operations and found 0.27 per cent of fatal pulmonary embolism.

Although there exist statistics where the mortality from thrombo-embolic diseases is as low as 0.1 per cent, as in the 29,000 operations of Gordon Watson (1924) in London and the 12,222 of Ranzi and Huber (1935) in Innsbruck, as well as other series where the mortality is 0.5 per cent, as in the 24,816 operations of Petrén (1941) in Sweden and the 18,668 of Dahl-Iversen and Ramberg (1932) in Denmark, nevertheless, it may be asserted that *until recently there occurred one death from thrombo-embolism in every 400 operations.*

The Frequency of Thrombosis and Pulmonary Embolism Following Childbirth and after Operations.

The frequency, as well as the course, of this disease is different after delivery and after operations. After delivery the frequency is lower and the course milder, owing to the greater resistance of the vascular system at that age. The patients submitted to operations are mostly elderly people.

The frequency of thrombo-embolism as well as the mortality within the two groups are therefore treated separately.

Thrombosis and embolism after childbirth.

The material in Table XXVI reveals that the incidence of thrombo-embolism after childbirth is about 1 per cent. Nürnberger's larger series of German cases (1934) of 179,000 deliveries between 1901 and 1934 gave a frequency of 1.3 per cent. If the series of Holzmann, Mikuliz-Radecki, Braun, Nettelblad, Hellsten and Schaanning are grouped together, a total of 167,761 cases, there are 1,695 instances of thrombosis, or a frequency of 1.01 per cent. These figures are quite sufficient to give a true picture of the field.

Thrombosis and pulmonary embolism after surgical operations.

The frequency of thrombo-embolism after operations is much more difficult to estimate. This figure is extremely variable, according to the age of the patients, the type of operation, the surgeon and the hospital. The variation in

TABLE XXVI. The Frequency of Thrombosis and Embolism after Childbirth. (Hellsten 1942.)

Author	Place	Years	Cases	Thrombosis Number	Thrombosis Per cent of total	Pulmonary embolism Number	Pulmonary embolism Per cent of Cases of thrombosis	Pulmonary embolism Per cent of total	Fatal pulmonary embolism Number	Fatal pulmonary embolism Per cent of Cases of thrombosis	Fatal pulmonary embolism Per cent of Embolic cases	Fatal pulmonary embolism Per cent of total
Holzman, M (1924)	Zürich	1903–1922	34,041	211	0.62	40	20.4	0.126	9	4.3	44	0.026
Bunzel, E. (1927)	New York	1927	31,716	—	—	—	—	0.1	—	—	—	0.065
Mikuliz-Radecki (1941)	Königsberg	1926–1938	16,482	355	2.15	59	16.6	0.36	8	2.3	13.6	0.049
Braun, H. (1939)	Cologne	1929–1938	20,674	183	0.89	20	10.9	0.10	9	4.9	45	0.045
Nürnberger, L. (1934)	Germany	1901–1934	170,072	2411	1.3	—	—	—	74	—	—	—
		1905–1934	201,824	—	—	—	—	—	—	—	—	0.03
Nettelblad, Å. (1931)	Stockholm, South. Mat. Hosp.	1912–1927	51,059	434	0.85	36	8.3	0.071	11	2.5	30	0.022
Hellsten, W. O. (1942)	Stockholm, Gener. Mat. Hosp.	1930–1939	36,180	420	1.16	150	35.7	0.041	20	4.76	13.3	0.074
Schaanning, G. (1924)	Christiania, Norway	1917–1923	9,367	57	0.61	13	22.8	0.14	—	—	—	—

TABLE XXVII. The Frequency of Thrombosis and Embolism after Surgical and Gynaecological Operations and Internal Diseases. (Hellsten 1942.)

Author	Place	Years	Surgical operations	Internal diseases	Thrombosis		Pulmonary embolism			Fatal pulmonary embolism			
					Number	Per cent of total	Number	Per cent of Cases of thrombosis	Per cent of total	Number	Per cent of Cases of thrombosis	Per cent of Embolic cases	Per cent of total
Scheidegger, W. (1928)	—	—	20,779	—	—	—	143	—	0.69	—	—	—	—
Singer, B. (1929)	Leipzig	1912–1913	—	15,429	198	1.28	98	49.5	0.64	21	10.6	21.4	0.136
		1926–1928	—	18,669	542	2.9	218	40.2	1.17	122	22.5	56.0	0.65
Braun, H. (1939)	Cologne	1929–1938	12,510 (Gyn.-op.)	—	89	0.71	23	25.8	0.18	21	23.6	91.3	0.17
Ranzi, E. and Huber, P. (1935)	Vienna	1901–1934	47,120	—	595	1.26	339	57.0	0.72	120	20.0	35.4	0.25
Ranzi, E. and Huber, P. (1935)	Innsbruck	1925–1931	12,222	—	126	1.0	68	54.0	0.56	14	11.0	—	0.10
Barker, Nygaard, Walters and Priestley	Mayo Clinic, Rochester U. S. A.	1928–1940	158,200	—	1,665	0.95	897	53.8	0.57	343	20.6	38.5	0.22

Giertz, K. H. and Crafoord, C. (1928–29)	Mörby, Sweden	1922–1927	7,824	—	239	3.1	—	—	—	38	**15.9**	—	0.32
Petrén, G. (1930)	Lund, Sweden	1922–1928	3,363	—	—	—	—	—	—	78	—	—	0.23
Petrén, G. (1941)	Lund, Sweden	1929–1938	24,816	—	—	—	—	—	—	133	—	—	0.54
Linde, S. (1941)	Stockholm, Sweden	1934–1939	11,401	—	259	2.3	107	41.3	0.94	41	**15.8**	38.3	0.36
Nicolaysen. J. (1931-32)	Norway	1930	21,867	—	335	1.53	—	—	—	—	—	—	—
Dahl-Iversen, E. and Ramberg, E. (1932)	Copenhagen, Kommunehospitalet, Denmark	1911–1930	18,168	—	636	3.5	423	66.5	2.33	95	**14.9**	22.5	0.52

different areas of a country is particularly striking. Thus in Sweden, thrombosis is rare in the northern provinces as compared with the frequency in the larger cities and the southern section of the country with its fairly wealthy agricultural population. On the contrary, thrombosis is more common in the northern part of the United States than in the South (Allen, Linton and Donaldson 1945). In general it may be said that operations in the out-patient department, as well as operations on the head, upper extremities and thorax show an extremely low frequency of thrombosis, while abdominal operations, particularly gynaecological ones and operations on the prostate, are known for their high frequency of thrombosis. In gynaecological operations the figure may be as high as 4 to 5 per cent. Thus Albers in 1942 reported a variation between 1.5 per cent in normal deliveries, 4.13 per cent after Caesarean sections and 17.85 per cent in cases where a high forceps had been applied. Counseller and McKinon (1942) found 3.4 per cent of post-operative thrombophlebitis after 1,920 total abdominal hysterectomies and 4.3 per cent after 764 similar subtotal operations. Table XXVII summarizes various surgical statistics.

As is shown in the table, the frequency of thrombosis was in some quarters as low as 1 per cent, even in surgical series, as was the case over a long period of time (1901 to 1934) in the Austrian clinics in Vienna and Innsbruck (von Eiselsberg) and at the Mayo Clinic, Rochester. On the other hand, in some Scandinavian series, this figure was as high as 1.5 per cent for Nicolaysen, Norway (1931—32) in 21,867 operations, 2.3 per cent in a series of 11,401 operations compiled by Linde (1934—39), 3.1 per cent for Giertz and Crafoord, Sweden (1922—27) in 7,800 operations, and 3.5 per cent for Dahl-Iversen and Ramberg, Denmark (1911—30) in 18,168 operations.

The statistical series presented here give a true picture of the conditions which prevailed in the surgical clinics of different countries prior to the introduction of the principles of free mobilization and early ambulation of the patients and of anticoagulant therapy. Even if a great variation in the frequency of thrombosis was observed in different clinics, *it can, however, be said that in general about one per cent of the surgical cases were complicated by a deep venous thrombosis or a pulmonary embolism.*

Recent surgical statistics with a low frequency of thrombosis.

The figures given in Table XXVII do not, however, give a true picture of the present situation, because early free movements and early ambulation after operations have been introduced in most of the surgical clinics in many countries. As a consequence, the frequency of post-operative thrombosis and pulmonary embolism has been reduced to half or a third of its original level.

Thus Johansson and Holmdahl (1944) reported from Gothenburg, Sweden, during the period 1933—1944, a frequency of 0.54 per cent among 45,376 surgical patients, including 14,821 abdominal operations, and a mortality in thrombo-embolism of 0.18 per cent. There was a decrease from 0.68 per cent during 1933—1936 and 0.67 per cent during 1937—1940 to 0.21 per cent during 1941—1944. In fact, in 1944 the figure 0.025 per cent was found. An exactly identical figure, 0.56 per cent, was reported by Westerborn (1946) from the second surgical clinic in Gothenburg on an equally large material. In Stockholm, Ekblom reported on 19,000 surgical cases with 0.75 per cent of thrombo-embolic complications during the period 1940—44, and in Örebro, Felländer found during 1932—1941 0.62 per cent of thrombosis and 0.14 per cent of fatal pulmonary embolism among 36,489 surgical patients. Of the patients with thrombo-embolism in these series 34, 22, 21 and 23 per cent respectively died.

A comprehensive survey of this subject was made by Backer-Gröndahl (1944) in Bergen, Norway. Since 1937 early free movement and ambulation as soon as possible before the end of the fourth day after operation, was applied at the City Hospital of Bergen. The author refers to the previous literature, particularly to the work of von Jaschke (1937), in which he demonstrated that the frequency of thrombosis can be reduced from 2.63 per cent to 0.6 per cent

by means of systematic respiratory exercises, free mobility
in bed and ambulation, if possible, on the day after operation. During the periods to be compared before and after
1937 there had been only minor changes in the kinds of
operation, operation technique, anaesthetics and the age of
the patients. For the evaluation of the results only three
groups of diseases were selected, namely, cancer of the
stomach (177 cases), gastric ulcer and duodenal ulcer (611
cases) and non-strangulated inguinal and femoral hernia in
patients over 20 years of age (1,017). A comparison of the
late with the early ambulation patients showed that the
frequency of both thrombosis and pulmonary embolism fell
to about one-third in the latter group. The length of stay
in hospital after operation was reduced by 30—50 per cent.

In Denmark Dahl-Iversen (1945) reported a similar experience. During the last three years all the patients were
allowed to get up and sit in a chair as early as 24 hours
after operation. On the second day the time out of bed
was extended and on the third day the patients moved about
freely. During this period there occurred 10 thrombo-embolic
complications after 1,736 operations (0.58 per cent), whereas
the same author, in 1932 collected 636 cases of thrombosis
after 18,168 similar operations (3.5 per cent) during the
years 1911—1930. There were no post-operative complications due to the early ambulation of the patients.

The influence of medical gymnastics performed in bed
on the frequency of thrombosis in the puerperium was
studied by Mortens (1942) at the maternity clinic of Rigs-
hospitalet, Copenhagen. During the years 1936 to 1942
different principles of treatment were applied in two
departments. In one of them the patients stayed in bed
until the 8th day. In the second medical gymnastics and
exercises were given in uncomplicated cases from the second
day on, according to an elaborate scheme, but in complicated
cases, as soon as possible. The patients in the latter department started walking on the 4th day and were discharged
on the 8th day. Each group included 10,000 patients. In
the former group the frequency of thrombosis was 2.68 per

cent and in the latter 1.65 per cent. Deep venous thrombosis occurred in 1 and 0.54 per cent, respectively.

In Switzerland the influence of preventive measures on the frequency of thrombosis after childbirth and gynaeco-logical operations has been studied by Koller (1942). At the maternity clinic of the University of Zürich the frequency varied between 1922 and 1938 from 1 to 1.7 per cent, 1 per cent after normal childbirth and 2.6 per cent after ope-rative procedures (7.2 per cent after Caesarean sections). After 1938 different preventive measures were applied in-cluding particular care in the operative technique, medical gymnastics in bed and early ambulation. From that year on, the frequency of thrombosis ranged between 0.75 per cent (one year) and 0.5 per cent (three years)).

TABLE XXVIII

The Frequency of Thrombosis and Embolism after Surgical Opera-tions and Childbirth in Patients Allowed Free Mobility and Early Ambulation.

Author	Place	Years	Surgi-cal cases	Thrombosis		Fatal pulmo-nary embolism		
				Number	Per cent of the whole material	Number	Per cent of	
							Thrombosis	The whole material
Johansson and Holm-dahl	Gothenburg	1933–1944	45,376	246	0.54	83	**34**	0.18
Westerborn	Gothenburg	1931–1944	43,737	254	0.56	56	**22**	0.13
Ekblom	Stockholm	1940–1944	19,000	143	0.75	30	**21**	0.16
Felländer	Örebro	1932–1941	36,489	226	0.62	52	**23**	0.14
Zilliacus	Stockholm	1940–1945	126,524	646	0.51	132	**20.4**	0.105
Dahl-Iversen	Copenhagen	1942–1944	1,736	10	0.58	—	—	—
Koller	Zürich	1938–1942	—	—	About 0.5	—	—	—

The present frequency of thrombosis in surgical cases is presumably fairly accurately expressed in the figures presented in Table XXVIII, where the incidence during the last few years in five of the above mentioned Scandinavian clinics is given.

One in every 170 patients, 0.6 per cent of the surgical cases, still develop thrombo-embolic complications. It is thus possible to reduce the frequency of post-operative thromboses to one-half or one-third of the original figures by appropriate means in the post-operative stage, but not to eliminate thrombosis and pulmonary embolism completely.

However, the mortality of thrombosis has remained at its original level, above 20 per cent. And it is likely to remain at that level as long as regular therapy with anticoagulants is not applied.

The Frequency of Thrombosis in Medical Cases.

Since the main cause of thrombosis is the recumbent position in bed with the slowing of the venous circulation, thrombi are almost as common in medical as in surgical wards. They are more often seen in patients with cardiovascular disorders, anaemia, dehydration, pneumonia or septic conditions. Vascular changes in elderly people also cause coronary and cerebral thrombosis.

Singer (1929) reported from Leipzig between the years 1912 and 1928, among the 6—8,000 patients treated annually at the medical clinic, a frequency of 1.5—0.97 per cent in 1912—1913, a figure which in 1926—1928 rose to 2.9 per cent. The mortality was 0.15 per cent during the previous period, 0.6 per cent during the latter.

Bauer (1946), in studying the official records of ten of the largest general hospitals in Sweden, found a total of 804 cases of thrombosis during the year 1939 in the general surgical and medical sections. In 448 cases, or 56 per cent of the total number, the disease was found in medical cases, and of these, 79 patients died, giving a death rate of 18 per cent.

Axhausen (1929) found in Stettin, in 11,266 autopsies from the period 1912—28, thrombosis in 6.9 per cent and pulmonary embolism in 3.39 per cent of the cases, with an equal distribution between the medical and the surgical cases. Belt (1934) and Breslich (1938) found pulmonary embolism even more common in persons dying of medical diseases than in those dying after operations. Hunter et. al. (1939), also, found little difference in the incidence between the medical and the surgical cases after a careful examination of the calf veins in 351 autopsies, with thrombosis in the veins in not less than 52.7 per cent of the cases.

As complications, thrombosis and pulmonary embolism are thus as common among the medical patients as among surgical ones.

The Percentage of Deaths among Cases of Thrombo-Embolism.

The preceding statistics have been included in the tables to allow of an evaluation of the incidence and mortality of pulmonary embolism. For convenience, the cases of thrombosis in these tables are assembled in a special table (XXIX).

Although the actual diagnosis of thrombosis and particularly of pulmonary embolism is very uncertain and often arbitrarily made, the above table does give some conception of the frequency of embolism in cases of thrombosis.

As is shown in the table, surgical thrombosis gives rise to pulmonary embolism in 50 to 60 per cent of cases, while obstetrical thrombosis gives a lower frequency, only 15 to 35 per cent.

The difference in mortality between obstetrical and surgical series is particularly striking. *In the surgical series, almost 20 per cent of the thrombosis cases die, while in the obstetrical series, the figure is only 3 to 5 per cent.* These figures are based on the findings in 4,445 surgical and 1,169 obstetrical cases of thrombosis.

TABLE XXIX

*The Frequency of Pulmonary Embolism and Deaths in Cases of
Thrombosis in the Large Statistical Series of the Literature.*
(After Hellsten.)

| | No. of cases of thrombosis | Pulmonary embolism | | Fatal pulmonary embolism | | |
		No. of cases	Percentage	No. of cases	Percentage of all cases of thrombosis	Percentage of all cases of pulmonary embolism
Surgical cases:						
Scheidegg, Singer, Braun, Ranzi	1,550	746	48.1	298	19.2	40.0
Barker, Nygaard,Walters and Priestley	1,665	897	53.8	343	20.6	38.5
Linde, Nicolaysen, Dahl-Iversen and Ramberg	1,230	740	60.1	166	15.5	24.4
Obstetrical cases:						
Holzmann, Mikuliz-Radecki, Braun	749	119	15.8	26	3.47	21.9
Hellsten	420	150	35.8	20	4.76	13.3

**The frequency of deep venous thrombosis and deaths caused by
pulmonary embolism in Sweden.**

The Swedish hospitals reported the mortality for the
cases of thrombosis to be about 9 (mean 8.7) per cent for the
years 1920, 1921, 1931 to 1940 (Table XXX). The real
figure is for various reasons considered to have been higher.

Cases with superficial venous thrombi were not included
in these figures, and in general, coronary and cerebral thrombi
were also reported separately, at least from the larger
clinics.

TABLE XXX

Cases of Deep Venous Thrombosis and the Mortality in this Disease According to the Annual Reports of Swedish Hospitals to the Royal Medical Board in 1920, 1921, 1931 to 1940.

Year	No. of cases	No. of deaths	Percentage of deaths
1920	846	80	9.46
1921	928	86	9.27
1931	2,380	230	9.66
1932	2,521	189	7.50
1933	2,746	218	7.94
1934	2,958	240	8.11
1935	3,125	226	7.23
1936	2,773	218	7.86
1937	2,950	333	11.28
1938	3,299	261	7.91
1939	3,055	262	8.57
1940	3,214	296	9.14

The great increase in the number of reported cases during recent years is due only to the increase in the number of hospitals.

The 3,214 cases of thrombo-embolism reported for 1940 occurred in a series of 376,571 patients, including 52,500 cases of childbirth, in all the hospitals of Sweden.

Most cases of thrombosis used to be taken care of at home. Taking into consideration that a larger number of such patients, at least in country districts, are still cared for at home, and that in the 100,000 deliveries there are 1,000 cases of thrombosis, it is justifiable to expect *at least 5,000 cases of deep venous thrombosis each year among the 6.3 million inhabitants of Sweden.*

Thus in 1940 about 0.8 per cent of the patients admitted to hospital in Sweden developed thrombo-embolism. According to the preceeding estimation, 0.8 per thousand of the entire population of the country develop this disease annually.

Duration of Recumbency Due to Thrombosis.

Although some surgeons in recent years have advised active movements and getting the patient out of bed as soon as possible, even in established and advanced thrombosis, the general practice has been in accordance with the opinion Morawitz expressed in 1934: "The less active the treatment, the better. Much activity is harmful. Rest is still the best treatment." Even if it had been desirable, it was not possible to let patients get up on account of the tenderness and pain. Usually the patient was kept in bed two weeks after the acute symptoms with fever had receded. The recumbency due to thrombosis was therefore in the older statistical series rather long, just as long in the obstetrical as in the surgical cases.

In Nettelblad's series the time in bed exceeded the normal time by an average of 43 days in 98 cases with thrombosis of the deep veins, by 49 days in 13 cases with pelvic thrombosis, and by 11 days in 296 cases with superficial thrombophlebitis. In Linde's series (1941) of 259 surgical cases of thrombosis the period in bed was 55 days as compared with the normal 17 days in uncomplicated cases. In Hellsten's series (420 obstetrical cases of thrombosis) the period in bed averaged 55.2 days. In Schaanning's obstetric series with 55 cases of thrombosis, the average time in bed was 52 days, while in Dahl-Iversen and Ramberg's surgical series with 636 cases of thrombosis, the corresponding figure was 30 days. These periods are calculated from the day of delivery or operation.

Even as late as 1940—45, Zilliacus (1946) found the mean recumbency time in 214 conservatively treated cases to be 36.3 days after the appearance of the symptoms.

As these series, comprising fifteen hundred cases, show, the period in bed in surgical as well as in obstetric cases of deep venous thrombosis or pulmonary embolism was under the earlier conservative treatment, as applied in Scandinavian countries and in Germany, prolonged by an average of 6 weeks.

The Social Significance of the Sequelae of Thrombosis.

Patients with indurated or ulcerated legs frequently have a history of previous thrombosis but the importance of the relationship between the two conditions is not widely recognised. Thus Howard (1945), tracing the medical history of these conditions back to Hippocrates, claimed that "75 per cent of the ulcers are upon the basis of varicose veins and venous stagnation" without adding anything further about the primary cause. He reported on successful treatment of the cases with venous ligation and post-surgical measures.

Bauer (1942), on the other hand, found induration in not less than 117 and ulcers in 90 out of 145 patients on re-examination of them more than 10 years after the attack of thrombosis.

Birger (1946), who studied the aetiology in 281 cases of ulcers of the leg, found the cause to be an earlier thrombosis in at least 44 per cent of the cases (personal communication). He found, in compiling the material from the State Pensions Bureau, that these ulcers were a greater cause of disability than diabetes and tuberculosis of bones and joints.

In addition to the pain and discomfort for the patient, the disabling ulcers are a considerable financial burden on the community.

In Denmark, different authors, physicians, and physiologists have studied the question of the medical treatment and the social significance of the disabling ulcers of the leg.

In his monograph on varicose veins and haemorrhoids Meisen (1932), in co-operation with Krogh and Rehberg paid considerable attention to the physio-pathology of the vascular system of the lower extremities. Deep venous thrombosis was stated to be the cause of varicose dilations of veins in a certain number of cases.

The whole question of the frequency and social significance of pathological changes of that kind in the lower extremities was studied by Roholm (1937). Since 75 per cent of the adult population (2.8 millions) at that time subscribed to health insurance funds, the significance of this disease could be fairly readily estimated. From 1931—35 there were 316 such cases annually in the hospitals of Copenhagen. According to an approximate estimation, there were 15,000 new cases each year in Denmark. The health insurance funds paid out in 1936 about 220,000 crowns, or 2 per cent of all daily sickness allowances. The hospital expenses of those cared for in such institutions amounted to 500,000 crowns, calculated on the basis of 8 crowns per day and a hospital stay of 40 days. The value of the lost working days, calculated as low as 5 crowns per day, amounted to 1,250,000 crowns. In addition, the State paid out the sum of 100,000 crowns in life annuities to 144 persons suffering from disability of this origin. Altogether, the disease in question cost the public in Denmark in 1936 about 2 million crowns, or approximately half a million dollars.

At the 15th Congress of German Dermatologists, 1928, Merz made the statement that "in Germany more working power is lost through the varicose symptom complex (ulcer and eczema) than through tuberculosis". At a rough estimate, he claimed that in Germany 500,000 persons were suffering from these lesions (Meisen 1932).

Social Aspects of the Application of Anticoagulant Therapy in Thrombosis.

The preceding study gives an account of the social significance of thrombo-embolism.

About 1 per cent of all the patients in surgical clinics suffer from thrombosis in the deep veins of the leg or from pulmonary embolism, a figure which, through active postoperative care, can be reduced to an average of 0.6 per cent. In Sweden every year approximately 0.8 per cent of the patients admitted to hospital suffer from thrombosis or pulmonary embolism.

The hospital stay used to be prolonged by about 6 weeks if a thrombo-embolic complication occurred.

A few years ago, about 3,000 cases of thrombosis were

reported from the hospitals of Sweden annually. With an average 6-week prolongation of the hospital stay because of thrombosis and a daily cost of 5 dollars, the annual loss will be 600,000 dollars. The lost working days are not in-cluded in this sum. With conservative treatment, fifteen to twenty per cent of the thrombosis patients in the surgical and medical clinics succumbed to pulmonary embolism and 4—5 per cent of those in obstetric and gynaecological clinics. In fact, one must expect about 5,000 cases of thrombosis annually. In a population of 6.3 millions not less than 300, probably about 500, deaths from this disease occur annually, the cases with coronary and cerebral thrombosis not being included in these figures.

In comparison, it may be mentioned that annually 400—500 persons were killed among the 5,000—6,000 injured in motor car accidents during 1937—39 in Sweden. There is every reason to assume that in general the permanent dis-ability in the legs of the 5,000 new cases of thrombosis which occurred annually were more severe than the sequelae arising in people surviving motor car accidents.

The social significance of the sequelae of thrombosis can, in fact, hardly be fully estimated. Every year several thousand persons will acquire circulatory disturbances in the lower extremities, swollen, painful, indurated legs, possibly also ulcers.

The value of the specific anticoagulant therapy should be seen against this background.

By early diagnosis and an adequate anticoagulant therapy all the above mentioned sequelae of spontaneous thrombosis can be eliminated.

Through the introduction of the specific therapy in cer-tain clinics in Sweden, the mortality has, in fact, dropped to less than one-tenth of the original figure. Pulmonary embolism and extension of the thrombosis to the other leg has been prevented. The hospital stay has been shortened from about 6 weeks to 5—10 days, and the frequency of complications such as induration of the leg and ulcers strikingly reduced. In a series of conservatively treated cases the thrombosis originating in the calf reached the thigh in 80 per cent, causing phlegmasia alba dolens and late disability. With early diagnosis and immediate heparin therapy the process was in a large series of cases limited to the calf in 80 per cent of the cases, leaving a normal leg for the future.

Bibliography.

Monographs and summarizing papers on heparin.

Astrup, T. Biochemistry of blood coagulation. — Copenhagen 1944 and Acta Physiol. Scand. 7, Suppl. 21, 1944.

Best, C. H. Heparin and thrombosis. — Harvey Lectures 36, 66, 1940—41.

Grimberg, A. and Mlle Krauss L'Héparine. Proprietes-utilisation. La Presse Medicale 47, 158, 1939.

Grüning, W. Das Heparin und seine klinische Anwendung z. Prophylaxe und Therapie d. Thrombose. — Klin. Wochenschr. 20, 921, 1941.

Hellsten, W. O. Phlebographic studies and heparin treatment in thromboembolic diseases. — Acta Chir. Scand. 86, Suppl. 73, 1942.

Jorpes, E. Heparin. Oxford University Press 1939.

v. Kaulla, N. Moderne Thrombosebekämpfung. — Verdinand Enke, Stuttgart 1946.

Mason, M. F. Heparin. A review of its history, chemistry, physiology and clinical applications. — Surgery 5, 451, 618, 1939.

Piper, J. Farmakologiske Undersøgelser over Synthetiske Koagulationshemmende Stoffer av Heparingruppen. — Dissertation Copenhagen 1945.

Quick, A. J. The Hemorrhagic Diseases, Springfield Ill. 1942.

Rivista Clinica Espanola 2, No. 1. 74, 1941. Editorial paper.

Zilliacus, H. On the specific treatment of thrombosis and pulmonary embolism with anticoagulants, with particular reference to the post-thrombotic sequelae. — Acta Medica Scandinavica, Suppl. 171, 1946.

References.

Adler, O. and Wiechowski, W. (1922) Arch. f. exp. Path. u. Pharm. *92*, 22.

Albers, D. (1942) Klin. Wochenschr. *21*, I, 600.

Allen, A. W., Linton, R. R., and Donaldson, G. A. (1943) Ann. Surgery *118*, 728; (1945) J. Amer. Med. Ass. *128*, 397.

Allen, E. V., Barker, N. W., and Waugh, J. M. (1942) J. Amer. Med. Ass. *120*, 1009.

Anschütz, R. (1903) Ber. d. deutsch. Chem. Ges. *36*, 465.

—»— (1909) Ann. d. Chemie *367*, 169.

Apitz, K. (1942) Erg. inn. Med. und Kinderheilkunde *61*, 54.

Astrup, T. and Astrup, I. (1938) Enzymologia *6*, 64.

Astrup, T. (1938) Enzymologia *5*, 12.

—»— (1944) Acta Physiol. Scand. *7*, suppl. 21.

—»—, Galsmar, I., and Volkert, M. (1944) Acta Physiol. Scand. *8*, 215.

Astrup, P. (1945) Nord. Med. *25*, 195.

Atlas, L. N. (1942) Surg. Gyn. Obst. *74*, 236.

Axhausen, H. (1929) Virchows Archiv *274*.

Backer-Gröndahl, N. (1944) Acta Chir. Scand. *91*, 193.

Bahls, G. (1940) Med. Klin. *36*, 216, 245.

Baker, E. C., and Sedwitz, S. H. (1943) Radiol. *41*, 451.

Bancroft, Fr. W. (1945) Ann. of Surgery *121*, 175.

Barker, N. W. and Counseller, V. S. (1939) Am. J. Obst. Gyn. *37*, 644.

Barker, N. W., Nygaard, K. K., Walters, W., and Priestley, J. T. (1940) Proc. Staff Meet. Mayo Clin. *15*, 769; (1941) *16*, 1, 17, 33.

Barker, N. W., Cromer, H. E., Hurn, M., and Waugh, J. M. (1945) Surgery *17*, 207.

Barratt, J. O. W. (1926/27) Brit. J. Exp. Path. *7*, 127.

—»— (1927) Journ. Physiol. *64*, 47.

Bauer, G. (1940) Acta Chir. Scand. *84*, Suppl. 61.

—»— (1941 a) Acta Med. Scand. *107*, 136; (1941 b) Arch. of Surg. *43*, 462.

—»— (1942) a) Acta Chir. Scand. *86*, 267; (1942 b) *86*, suppl. 74.

—»— (1944) Acta Chir. Scand. *90*, 229.

—»— (1945) Acta Radiol. *26*, 577.

—»— (1946 a) Lancet 250 March 3 p. 447; (1946 b) J. Amer. Med. Ass. May 18.

Beaser, S. B., Segel, A., and Vandam, L. (1942) J. Clin. Invest. *21*, 447.

Belt, T. H. (1934) Am. J. Path. *10*, 129.

Bergström, S. (1935) Naturwiss. *23*, 706.

— » — (1936) Zeitschr. physiol. Chem. *238*, 163.

— » —, Jorpes, E., and Wilander, O. (1937) Skand. Arch. Physiol. *76*, 175.

Berseus, S. (1938) Nord. Med. Tidskr. *16*, 1599.

Best, C. H. (1938) Brit. Med. J. II, Nov. 12, 977.

Best, C. H., Cowan, C., and MacLean, D. L. (1937) Science *85*, 338.

— » — (1938) J. Physiol. *92*, 20.

Bierman, W., and Baehr, G. (1941) J. Amer. Med. Ass. *116*, 292.

Bingham, J. B., Meyer, O. O., and Pohle, F. J. (1941) Amer. J. Med. Sc. *202*, 563.

Birger, I. (1941) Nord. Med. *12*, 3542.

— » — (1947) Acta Chir. Scand. Supplem.

Blitstein, S. (1935) Rev. Belg. Sc. Med. *7*, 69.

Blix, G. (1937) Zeitschr. physiol. Chem. *219*, 82.

Boland, E. W., and Rooney, H. M. (1941) Western J. Surg. Obst. Gyn. *49*, 356.

Bollman, J. L., and Preston, F. W. (1942) J. Amer. Med. Ass. *120*, 1021.

Boström, K. G., and William-Olsson, L. (1938) Lancet, *2*, July 9, 78.

Boyd, E. M., and Murray, R. B. (1937) J. Biol. Chem. *117*, 629.

Boys, F. (1942) Surgery *11*, 118.

Brambel, C. E., and Loker, F. F. (1944) Arch. of Surgery *48*, 1.

Brambel, C. E. (1945) Arch. of Surgery *50*, 137.

Breslich, P. J. (1938) Journal-Lancet *58*, 445.

Brinkhous, K. M., Smith, H. P., Warner, E. D., and Seegers, W. H. (1939) Am. J. Physiol. *125*, 683.

Bruzelius, S. (1945) Acta Chir. Scand. *92*, Suppl. 100.

Brychonenko, S., and Steppuhn, O. (1923) Biochem. Zeitschr. *140*, 1.

Bryson, J. C., and Code, C. F. (1944) Proc. Staff Meet. Mayo Clinic *19*, 100.

Bunzel, E. E. (1927) Am. J. Obst. Gyn. *13*, 584.

Butsch, W. L., and Stewart, J. D. (1942) J. Amer. Med. Ass. *120*, 1025.

Butt, H. R., Allèn, E. V., and Bollman, J. L. (1941) Proc. Staff Meet. Mayo Clinic *16*, 388.

Buxton, R. W., Farris, J. M., Moyer, C. A., and Coller, F. A. (1944) Surgery *15*, 749.

Campbell, H. A., Roberts, W. L., Smith, W. K., and Link, K. P. (1940) J. Biol. Chem. *136*, 47.

Campbell, H. A., Smith, W. K., Roberts, W. L., and Link, K. P. (1941) J. Biol. Chem. *138*, 1.

Campbell, H. A., and Link, K. P. (1941) J. Biol. Chem. *138*, 21.

Chargaff, E., Bancroft, F. W., and Stanley-Brown, M. (1936) J. Biol. Chem. *115*, 149, 155.

Chargaff, E., and Olson, K. B. (1938) J. Biol. Chem. *122*, 153.

Charles, A. F., and Scott, D. A. (1933) J. Biol. Chem. *102*, 425, 437.

Charles, A. F., Scott, D. A., and Fischer, A. M. (1934) Trans. Roy. Soc. Canada, *28* Sect. 5, 49.

Charles, A. F., and Scott, D. A. (1936) Biochem. J. *30*, 1927.

Charles, A. F., and Todd, A. R. (1940) Biochem. J. *34*, 112.

Ciotola, G. (1945) Boll. Oculistica *28*, No 1—3, p. 35.

Clason, S. (1941) Acta Med. Scand. *107*, 131.

Collins, D. C. (1936) Am. J. Surg. N. S. *33*, 210.

Copley, A. L., and Schnedorf, J. G. (1941) Am. J. Physiol. *133*, 562.

Copley, A. L. (1941) Science *93*, 478.

Counseller, V. S., and McKinnon, D. A. (1942) Surg. Gyn. Obst. *75*, 114.

Crafoord, C. (1937) Acta Chir. Scand. *79*, 407.

—»— (1939) Acta Chir. Scand. *82*, 319.

—»— (1941) Acta Med. Scand. *107*, 116.

—»— (1942 a) Nord. Med. *13*, 527; (1942 b) *16*, 2836.

—»—, and Jorpes, E. (1941) J. Amer. Med. Ass. *116*, 2831.

Cutler, E. C., and Morton, J. J. (1917) Surg. Gyn. Obst. *25*, 621.

Cutler, E. C., and Hunt, A. M. (1922) Arch. Int. Med. *29*, 449.

Dahl-Iversen, E., and Ramberg, E. (1932) Hospitalstid. *75*, 1, 371.

Dahl-Iversen, E. (1945) Nord. Med. *28*, 2085.

Dale, D. U., and Jaques, L. B. (1942) Canad. Med. Ass. J. *46*, 546.

—»— (1945) Am. J. Physiol. *143*, 101.

Dam, H., Schønheyder, F., and Tage-Hansen, E. (1936) Biochem. J. *30*, 1075.

Dam, H., and Glavind, J. (1939) Skand. Arch. f. Physiol. *82*, 221.

Daughtry, de Witt C. (1945) Am. J. Surg. *108*, 80.

Demole, V., and Reinert, M. (1930) Arch. f. exp. Path. u. Pharm. *158*, 211.

Denecke, K. (1929) Münchner Med. Wochenschr. 76 : 2, 1912.

Doane, J. C. (1943) Ann. of. Internal Med. *19*, 634.

Dockeray, G. C., and Kawerau, E. (1940) Brit. Med. J. *2*, 703.

Doughtery, J., and Homans, J. (1940) Surg. Gyn. Obst. *71*, 697.

Dragstedt, C. A., Wells, J. A., and Rocha e Silva, M. (1942) Proc. Soc. Exp. Biol. Med. *51*, 191.

Duncan, R. D., and Myers, M. E. (1943) Amer. J. Surg. *102*, 34.

Dyckerhoff, H., and Goossens, N. (1939) Zeitschr. f. ges. exp. Med. *106*, 181.

Eagle, H., and Tzvee, N. H. (1937) J. Gen. Physiol. *20*, 543.

Ecker, E. E., and Pillemer, L. (1941) J. of Immunology *40*, 73.

Edlund, Y. (1946) Nord. Med. *29*, 223.

Ehrlich, P. (1877) Arch. f. mikr. Anat. *13*, 263.

Ehrström, R. (1943) Nord. Lærebog i Intern Medizin III. Copenhagen, 11.

Ekblom, T. (1946) Nord. Med. *29*, 348.

Elsner, H., Broser, W., and Bürgel, E. (1937) Zeitschr. physiol. Chem. *246*, 244.

Elsner, H. (1938) Zeitschr. physiol. Chem. *252*, 196.

Elson, L. A., and Morgan, W. T. J. (1933) Biochem. J. *27*, 1824.

Enghoff, H. (1938) Uppsala Univ. Årsskrift. 1937, *9*, 73.

Enocksson, B. (1931) Acta Med. Scand. *75*, 360.

—»—, Gjertz, A., Schnell, Å., and Torgersruud, T. (1936) Acta Med. Scand. *88*, 445.

Ershler, J. L., and Blaisdell, I. H. (1941) J. Amer. Med. Ass. *117*, 927.

Evans, J. A. (1944) S. Clin. North America *24*, 534.

—»— (1944) Connectic. St. Med. J. *8*, 71.

Fabricius-Møller, J., and Sørensen, Fr. (1945) Ugeskr. f. Læger *107*, 63.

Falconer, B. (1943) Sv. Läkartidn. *40*, 22.

von Falkenhausen, M. (1931) Z. ges. exp. Med. *79*, 18.
Farr, C. E., and Spiegel, R. (1929) Ann. of Surg. *89*, 481.
Felländer, M. (1943) Nord. Med. *17*, 182.
Ferguson, J. H. (1940) J. Lab. Clin. Med. *26*, 52.
—»— (1937/38) Proc. Soc. Exp. Biol. Med. *37*, 23.
Ferguson, R. R. (1941) J. Amer. Med. Ass. *117*, 1351.
Ficarra, B. J. (1944) Amer. J. Surg. *106*, 168.
Fine, J., and Sears, J. B. (1941) Ann. of Surg. *114*, 801.
Fine, J., and Starr, A. (1945) Surgery *17*, 232.
Fischer, A. (1927) Gewebezüchtung, 396.
—»— (1930) Pflügers Arch. *225*, 737.
—»— (1931) Biochem. Zeitschr. *240*, 364.
—»—, and Schmitz, A. (1932) Zeitschr. physiol. Chem. *210*, 129.
Fischer, A. (1932) Biochem. Zeitschr. *244*, 464.
—»—, and Schmitz, A. (1933) Zeitschr. physiol. Chem. *216*, 264, 274.
Fischer, A. (1935) Biochem. Z. *278*, 133.
—»— (1936) Protoplasma *26*, 344.
—»—, and Herrmann, H. (1937) Enzymologia *3*, 180.
Fischer, A. (1940) Med. Klin. *36*, 220.
Fletcher, C. M. (1940) Lancet *239*, 525.
—»— (1941) Ibid. I. *240*, 444.
Foster, R. H. K. (1942) J. Lab. Clin. Med. *27*, 820.
Franz, Fr. (1903) Arch. f. exp. Path. u. Pharm. *49*, 342.
Friedmann, M., Hamburger, W. W., and Katz, L. N. (1939) J. Amer. Med. Ass. *113*, 1702.
Friedmann, M. (1941) Arch. Int. Med. *67*, 921.
Frimann-Dahl, J. (1935) Acta Chir. Scand. *76*, Suppl. 36.
Frykholm, R. (1939) Nord. Med. *4*, 3534.
—»— (1940) Surg. Gyn. Obst. *71*, 307.
Fuchs, H. (1930) Biochem. Zeitschr. *222*, 470.
—»—, and Hartmann, E. (1928) Z. Immunitätsforsch. *58*, 1.
Fuchs, H. (1931) Z. ges. exp. Med. *79*, 35.
—»— (1933) Ergebn. d. Enzymforsch. *2*, 282.
Fuller, C. J. (1930) Lancet *218*, 115.
Fürth, O., Herrmann, H., and Scholl, R. (1934) Biochem. Zeitschr. *271*, 395.
Fåhraeus, R. (1921) The Suspension Stability of the Blood. Acta Med. Scand. *55*, 1.
Gamble, H. A. (1935) Amer. J. Surg. *28*, 93.
Ganes, J. (1942) Nord. Med. *16*, 2841.

Gauss (1934) Verhandl. d. deutsch. Ges. Kreislaufforsch. 7, 252.

Gardner, J. A., Gainsborough, H., and Murray, R. (1938) Biochem. J. 32, 1457.

Geissendörfer, G. (1930) Klin. Wochenschr. 9, 1, 737.

Giertz, K. H., and Crafoord, C. (1928—29) Acta Chir. Scand. 64, 121.

Glazko, A. J., and Ferguson, J. H. (1940) Proc. Soc. Exp. Biol. Med. 45, 43.

Goerner, A. (1930—31) J. Lab. Clin. Med. 16, 369.

Gordon-Watson, C. (1924) Brit. Med. J. 2, 854.

Gradle, H. S. (1937) Amer. J. Ophthalmol. 20, 1125.

Gratia, A. (1920) C. R. Soc. Biol. 83, 311.

Greene, R. (1943) J. Pathol. and Bact. 55, 259.

Gross, P. (1928—29) Proc. Soc. Exp. Biol. Med. 26, 393.

Groth, K. E. (1940) Surgery 8, 617.

Haas, G. (1928) Klin. Wochenschr. 7, 1356.

Hahn, P. F. (1943) Science 98, 19.

Ham, F. F. (1944) Western J. Surg. Obst. Gyn. 52, 129.

Ham, T. H., and Curtis, F. C. (1938) Medicine 17, 447.

Hambleton, A., and Christianson, R. A. (1939) Amer. J. Med. Sc. 198, 177.

Hammarsten, E. (1924) Biochem. Z. 144, 5—6.

Hammarsten, O. (1896) Zeitschr. f. physiol. Chem. 22, 333; (1899) 28, 98.

Hampton, H. H., and Wharton, L. R. (1920) Bull. Johns Hopkins Hosp. 31, 95.

Hanzlik, P. J., Butt, E. M., and Stockton, A. B. (1927) J. Immunol. 13, 409.

Haycraft, J. B. (1884) Arch. f. exp. Path. u. Pharm. 18, 209.

Hedenius, P., and Wilander, O. (1936) Acta Med. Scand. 88, 443.

Hedenius, P. (1936 a) Acta Med. Scand. 88, 440; (1936 b) 89, 263.

—»—, and Snellman, B. (1937) Nord. Med. Tidskr. 13, 914.

Hedenius, P. (1937) Nord. Med. Tidskr. 14, 1328.

—»— (1937) Lancet, Nov. 20th, 1186.

Hellsten, W. (1942) Acta Chir. Scand. 86, suppl. 73.

Herrmann, H. (1937) Skand. Arch. f. Physiol. 76, 125.

Hermansson, Å. (1925) Sv. Läkartidn. 22, 27.

de Hevesy, G. (1946) Les Prix Nobel 1940—44. Norstedt and Söner, Stockholm. p. 95.

Hiruma, K. (1923) Biochem. Z. 139, 152.

Holmgren, H., and Wilander, O. (1937) Zeitschr. f. mikro-anat. Forsch. *42*, 242.

Holmen, C. (1946) Ugeskr. f. Læger *108*, 48.

Holmin, N., and Ploman, K. G. (1938) Lancet March 19th, 664.

Holzmann, H. (1924) Schweiz. med. Wochenschr. *5*, 569.

Homans, J. (1934) New Engl. J. Med. *211*, 993.

—»— (1938) Intern. Abstr. of Surg. *18*, 533.

—»— (1939) Circulatory diseases of the extremities. New York.

—»— (1941) New England J. Med. *224*, 179.

—»— (1944) Surg. Gyn. Obst. *79*, 70.

Horwitt, M. K. (1940) Science *92*, 89.

Hosoi, K. (1932) Ann. Surg. *95*, 67.

Howard, M. A. (1945) Western J. Surg. Gyn. Obst. *53*, 217.

Howell, W. H. (1916—17) Harvey Lectures, Series XII.

—» —, and Holt, E. (1918) Am. J. of Physiol. *47*, 328.

Howell, W. H. (1922) Am. J. of Physiol. *63*, 434.

—»— (1924—25) Am. J. of Physiol. *71*, 553.

—»— (1928) Bull. Johns Hopkins Hospital *42*, 199.

—» —, and MacDonald, C. H. (1930) Bull. Johns Hopkins Hospital *46*, 365.

Huggett, A. S. G., and Silman, H. (1932) J. Physiol. *74*, 9.

—» —, and Rowe, F. M. (1933) J. Physiol. *78*, Proc. 25.

Hunter, W. C., Sneeden, V. D., Robertson, T. D., and Snyder, G. A. C. (1939) Arch. Int. Med. *68*, 1.

Hunter, W. C., Krygier, J. J., Kennedy, J. C., and Sneeden, V. D. (1945) Surgery *17*, 178.

Hübner, A., and Freudenberg, K. (1931) Chirurg. *3*, 324.

D'Ingiami, V. (1945) Arch. Surgery *50*, 214.

Ivy, A. C., Greengard, H., Stein, J. F., Grodius, F. S., and Dutton, D. F. (1943) Surg. Gyn. Obst. *76*, 85.

Jacob, F. (1945) Schweiz. med. Wochenschr. *75*, 208.

Jalling, O., Jorpes, E., and Lindén, G. (1946) Quarterly J. Pharm. & Pharmacol. *19*, 96.

Jansen, K. (1938) Nord. Med. *20*, 1993; (1944) Dikumarin, Copenhagen.

Jaques, L. B., Charles, A. F., and Best, C. H. (1938) Acta Med. Scand. Suppl. 90, 190.

Jaques, L. B. (1939) Am. J. of Physiol. *125*, 98.

—» —, and Waters, E. T. (1940) Am. J. of Physiol. *129*, 389.

Jaques, L. B. (1940 a) Science *92*, 488; (1940 b) J. Biol. Chem. *133*, 445.

Jaques, L. B., and Charles, A. F. (1941) Quarterly J. of Pharm. and Pharmacol. *14*, 1.
Jaques, L. B., Waters, E. T., and Charles, A. F. (1942) J. Biol. Chem. *144*, 229.
Jaques, L. B. and Mustard, R. A. (1940) Biochem. J. *34*, 153.
Jensen, V. A. (1936) Acta Ophthalmol. Suppl. 10.
Johansson, S. and Holmdahl, S. (1944) Nord. Med. *25*, 524.
Johnstone, D. F. (1945) Lancet *248*, Jan. 6, 9.
Jores, A., and Detzel, A. (1940) Klin. Wochenschr. *19*, 641.
Jorpes, E. (1935 a) Naturwiss. *23*, 196; (1935 b) Biochem. J. *29*, 1817.
—»— (1936) Acta Med. Scand. *88*, 427.
—»—, and Bergström, S. (1936) Zeitschr. physiol. Chem. *244*, 253.
—»— (1937) J. Biol. Chem. *118*, 447.
Jorpes, E. (1937) Nord. Med. Tidskr. *13*, 912.
—»—, Holmgren, H., and Wilander, O. (1937) Zeitschr. mikr.-anat. Forsch. *42*, 279.
Jorpes, E. (1938) Skand. Arch. f. Physiol. *80*, 202.
—»— (1941) Acta Med. Scand. *107*, 107.
—»— (1942 a) Biochem. J. *36*, 203.
—»— (1942 b) Nord. Med. *16*, 2833.
—»— (1942 c) Acta Obst. Gyn. Scand. *22*, Suppl. 2.
—»— (1943) Z. physiol. Chem. *278*, 7.
—»— (1946 a) Edinburgh Med. J. *53*, 222; (1946 b) Sv. Läkartidn. *43*, 1105; (1946 c) Nord. Med. *30*, 813.
Kahlson, G., and Landby, E. (1937) Skand. Arch. f. Physiol. *77*, 301.
Kallner, S., and Olsson, W. (1946) Sv. Läkartidn. *43*, 1121.
Karrer, P., Koenig, H., and Usteri, E. (1943) Helv. Chim. Acta *26*, 1296.
Karrer, P., Usteri, E., and Camerino, B. (1944) Helv. Chim. Acta *27*, 1422.
von Kaulla, K. N. (1939) Acta Med. Scand. *98*, 374.
—»— (1946) Moderne Thrombosebekämpfung. Ferd. Enke, Stuttgart.
Kelson, S. R. (1941) J. Amer. Med. Ass. *117*, 1349.
—»—, and White, P. D. (1939) J. Amer. Med. Ass. *113*, 1700.
Keyes, J. W., and Schaffer, C. F. (1942) J. Amer. Med. Ass. *119*, 882.
Killian, H. (1930) Klin. Wochenschr. *9*, 1, 730.

Knoll, H., and Schürch, O. (1938) Lancet, June 18th, 1387.
Kolff, W. J. (1939) Lancet 2, 1176.
—»— (1942) Ned. Tijdsihr. v. Geneesk. 86, 174.
—»— (1943 a) Acta Med. Scand. 114 : I, 92.
—»— (1943 b) Geneeskundige Gids 21.
—»— (1944) Acta Med. Scand. 117 : II, 121.
—»— (1946) De kunstmatige nier. Dissertatie, Groningen. Utgive K. & K. Kempen.
Koller, T. (1942) Schweiz. Med. Wochenschr. 72, 1008.
Kravitz, D. (1942) Amer. J. of Ophthalmol. 25 : 1, 1367.
Kuizenga, M. H., and Spaulding, L. B. (1943) J. Biol. Chem. 148, 641.
Kyes, P., and Strausser, E. R. (1926) J. Immunol. 12, 419.
König, W. (1942) Zentralblatt f. Chir. 69, 838.
Lam, C. R. (1941) Ann. of Surg. 114, 205.
—»— (1943) Surg. Clin. North Amer. 23, 1304.
Lampert, H. (1931) Die physikalische Seite des Blutgerinnungsproblems. G. Thieme, Leipzig.
Lange, H. (1946) Acta Med. Scand. Suppl. 176.
Lange, K., and Loewe, L. (1946) Surg. Gyn. Obst. 82, 256.
—»—, and Boyd, L. J. (1945) Surg. Gyn. Obst. 80, 346.
Larsson, S. (1942) Nord. Med. 16, 3350.
Laufman, H. (1942) Surg., Gyn. Obst. 74, 479.
—»—, and Heller, R. (1943) Surg., Gyn. Obst. 76, 655.
Leach, C. E., Faulkner, J. M., Duncan, C. N., McGinn, S., Porter, R. R., and White, P. D. (1941) J. Amer. Med. Ass. 117, 1345.
Lehman, E. P. (1940) Practitioner 144, 638.
—»—, and Boys, F. (1940) Ann. of Surg. 112, 969.
—»— (1940) Ann. of Surg. 111, 427.
—»— (1941) Arch. of Surg. 43, 933.
—»— (1942) Surgery, 12, 236.
Lehmann, J. (1942 a) Sv. Läkartidn. 39, 73 ; (1942 b) Ibid. 39, 1041.
—»— (1943) Lancet 244, 611.
Lehner, J. (1924) Ergeb. d. Anat. u. Entwicklungsgesch. 25, 67.
Leissner, S. H. (1942) Nord. Med. 13, 523.
—»— (1941) Acta med. Scand. 107, 127.
Leriche, R., and Kumlin, J. (1934) Presse méd. 42, 1481.
Leriche, R. (1938) J. Intern. de Chir. 3, 585.
Levene, P. A. (1925) Hexosamines and mucoproteins. New York.

Levison, L. A., and Roberts, J. L. (1942) Ohio State Med. J., *38*, 338.

Liavaag, K., and Nicolaysen, K. (1946) Tdskr. f. den Norske Lægeforen.

Lichtenstein, A. (1944) Nord. Med. *21*, 16.

Lichtman, S. S., and Bierman, W. (1941) J. Amer. Med. Ass. *116*, 286.

Linde, S. (1941) Acta Chir. Scand. *84*, 310.

—»— (1941) Acta Med. Scand. *107*, 165.

—»— (1944) Sv. Läkartidn. *41*, 1681.

Lindgren, S. (1939) Arch. klin. Chir. Kongressenber. d. deutsch. chir. Ges. April.

—»—, and Walldén, L. (1944) Acta Med. Scand. *117*, 417.

Lindgren, S., and Wilander, O. (1941) Acta Med. Scand. *107*, 148.

Link, K. P. (1944) Federation Proc. *4*, 176. Univ. of Wisconsin.

—»— (1945) Proc. Institute of Medicine, Chicago *15*, Oct. 15.

Linkberg, A. (1932) Z. ges. exp. Med. *85*, 262.

Lison, L. (1935 a) C. R. Soc. Biol. *118*, 821; (1935 b) Arch. de Biol. *46*, 599.

—»— (1936) Bull. Soc. Chem. Biol. *18*, 225.

Lithander, A. (1938) Nord. Med. Tidskr. *15*, 597.

Loeffler, L. (1926) Arch. f. exp. Path. u. Pharm. *117*, 189.

Loewe, L., Rosenblatt, P., Greene, H. J., and Russell, M. (1944) J. Amer. Med. Ass. *124*, 144.

Loewe, L., and Rosenblatt, P. (1944) Amer. J. Med. Sc. *208*, 54.

Loewe, L., Lange, K., and Boyd, L. J. (1945) Science *102*, 151.

Luke, J. C. (1943) Lancet *244*, 552.

Lyons, C. (1941) Ann. of Surg. *113*, 113.

MacIntosh, F. C. (1941 a) Biochem. J. *35*, 770; (1941 b) Ibid. *35*, 776.

MacNeal, W. J., Frisbee, F. C., and Blevins, A. (1943) Arch. Ophthalmol. *29*, 231.

MacQuigg, R. E. (1945) Surgery *18*, 592.

Magerl, J. F. (1942) Zeitschr. f. Immunitätsforsch. *101*, 1, 122, 168, 225.

Magnusson, H., and Ahnsjö, S. (1937) Acta Ped. Scand. *19*, 412.

Magnusson, H. (1938 a) Nord. Med. Tidskr. *16*, 1157; (1938 b) Acta Ped. Scand. *23*, 16; (1938 c) Lancet March 19, 666.

—»— (1940) Nord. Med. *8*, 2298.

—»—, and Lindahl, J. (1945) Sv. Läkartidn. *42*, 2739.

Magnusson, H., and Frisell, E. (1947) Acta med. scand. (In print.)

Magnusson, H. (1947) Acta Dermato-venerologica. (In print.)

Mann, F. C., and Bollman, J. L. (1939) Ann. rev. physiol. I, 288.

Martin, P. (1941) Brit. Med. J. Oct. 18, 537.

Martin, P. G. C. (1944) Brit. Med. J. Sept. 2, 308.

Mason, E. C. (1924) Surg. Gyn. Obst. *39*, 421.

McClure, R. D., and Harkins, H. N. (1942) Surgery *14*, 747.

McLean, J. (1916) Am. J. of Physiol. *41*, 250.

—»—, Meyer, B., and Griffith, J. (1941) J. Amer. Med. Ass. *117*, 1870.

Meisen, V. (1932) Varicose veins and hemorrhoids. Oxford Univ. Press, London, p. 116.

Mellanby, J. (1909) J. Physiol. *38*, 495.

—»— (1934) Proc. Roy. Soc. *116*, 1.

Meyer, K., and Palmer, J. W. (1936 a) J. Biol. Chem. *114*, Proc. 68; (1936 b) Ibid. *114*, 689.

Meyer, K., and Smyth, E. M. (1938) Cold Spring Harbor Symposia Quant. Biol. *62*, 47.

Miki, H., and Satani, H. (1935) Mitt. a. d. Med. Akad. zu Kioto *14*, 337.

Miller, E. R. (1940) Delaware State Med. J. *12*, 155.

Morawitz, P. (1904 a) Arch. f. klin. Med. *79*, 1, 25, 215; (1904 b) Hofmeisters Beiträge *4*, 381.

—»— (1934) Verhandl. d. deutsch. Ges. f. Kreislaufforsch. *7*, 80.

Mortens, J. (1944) Nord. Med. *21*, 93.

Muntarbhorn, S. (1945) Lancet *248*, Jan. 6, 10.

Murray, D. W. G., Jaques, L. B., Perrett, T. S., and Best, C. H. (1936) Canad. Med. Ass. J. *35*, 621; (1937) Surgery *2*, 163.

Murray, D. W. G., and Best, C. H. (1938 a) J. Amer. Med. Ass. *110*, 118; (1938 b) Ann. of Surg. *108*, 163.

Murray, D. W. G., and MacKenzie, R. (1939) Canad. Med. Ass. J. *41*, 38.

Murray, D. W. G. (1940 a) Brit. J. of Surg. *27*, 567; (1940 b) Surg. Gyn. Obst. *70*, 246; (1940 c) Arch. of Surg. *40*, 307.

—»—, and Janes, J. M. (1940) Brit. Med. J. *2*, 6.

Murray, D. W. G. (1941) Surg. Gyn. Obst. *72*, 340; (1943) Ibid. *77*, 157.

—»—, and MacKenzie, R. (1942) Amer. J. of Surg. N. S. *57*, 414.

Måhlén, S. (1942) Nord. Med. *16*, 3349.

Nasse, H. (1836) Das Blut, Bonn.

Nettelblad, Å. (1931) Acta Obst. Gyn. Scand. *11*, 165.

Neumann, R. (1938) Virchows Arch. *301*, 708.

Neuwirth, I. (1937) J. Biol. Chem. *120*, 463.

Newburger, B. (1943) Surgery *14*, 142.

Nicolaysen, J. (1931—32) Acta Chir. Scand. *69*, 21.

Nielsen, G. (1942) Acta Med. Scand. *111*, 66; (1943) Nord. Med. *20*, 1892.

—»—, and Rode-Møller, I. (1943) Acta Med. Scand. *113*, 464.

Nielsen, A. (1942) Nord. Med. *16*, 2873.

Nilzén, Å. (1945) Acta Chir. Scand. *92*, 285.

Nürnberger, L. (1927) Arch. f. Gynäk. (Kongr. Ber.) *132*, 106.

—»— (1934) Verhandl. d. deutsch. Ges. f. Kreisslauf-forsch. *7*, 101.

Ochsner, A. (1939) Surgery, *6*, 129.

—»— (1945) Surgery *17*, 240.

—»—, and de Bakey, M. (1939) Surgery *5*, 491.

—»— (1943) Surgery *14*, 679.

Ochsner, A., and Mahorner, H. R. (1935) Arch. of Surg. *31*, 308.

Odquist, B. (1942) Nord. Med. *16*, 3349.

Oehler, J. (1927) Münchn. med. Wochenschr. *74*, 1662.

Oelkers, H. A. (1940) Arch. f. exp. Path. u. Pharm. *194*, 477.

Oldfelt, C. O. (1942) Acta Med. Scand. *112*, 585, 593.

Olovson, T. (1939) Acta Chir. Scand. *82*, 487; (1942) Ibid. *86*, 463.

—»— (1940) Der Chirurg *12*, 316; (1944) Sv. Läkartidn. *41*, 2639.

Parson, W. H. (1945) Surg. Gyn. Obst. *81*, 79.

Pauly, H., and Lockemann, K. (1915) Ber. d. Chem. Ges. *48*, 28.

Payr, E. (1930) Zentralblatt f. Chir. *57*, I, 961.

Petrén, G. (1930) Ann. of Surg. *92*, 1; (1941) Chirurg. *13*, 529.

Piper, J. (1945) Farmakologiske Undersøgelser over Syntetiske Koagulationshæmmende Stoffer av Heparingruppen. Dissertation. Copenhagen.

—» —, and Astrup, T. (1945) Acta Physiol. Scand. *9*, 351.

Plass, E. D., and Rourke, D. M. (1928) J. Chir. Invest. *5*, 531.

Ploman, K. G. (1920) Ann. d'Oculist *157*, 569.

—» — (1938) Sv. Läkarsäll. Förhandl. 25 okt.

—» — (1938) Acta Ophthalmol. *16*, 502; (1943) Ibid. *21*, 190.

Ponder, E. (1934) The Mammalian Red Cell. Berlin 1934.

Potts, W. J. (1940) Ann. of Surg. *111*, 554; (1943) Arch. of Surg. *46*, 27.

—» —, and Smith, S. (1941) Arch. of Surg. *42*, 661.

Prandoni, A., and Wright, I. (1942) New York Acad. Med. *18*, 433.

Priestley, J. T., Essex, H. E., and Barker, N. W. (1941) Proc. Staff Meet. Mayo Clinic *16*, 60.

Priestley, J. T. and Barker, N. W. (1942) Surg. Gyn. Obst. *75*, 198.

de Puoz, J. (1938) Schweiz. med. Wochenschr. *68*, 524.

Putnam, F. W., and Neurath, H. (1945) J. Biol. Chem. *159*, 195.

Putzer, R. (1939) Arch. f. Gynäk. *169*, 444.

Quensel, U. (1933) Acta Path. Microbiol. Scand. Suppl. XVI, 358.

de Quervain, F. (1925) Schweiz. Med. Wochenschr. *6*, 497.

Quick, A. J. (1935) J. Immunol. *29*, 87; (1936) Am. J. Physiol. *115*, 317, *116*, 535.

—» — (1937) Am. J. Physiol. *118*, 260; (1938) Am. J. Physiol. *123*, 712.

—» —, Stanley-Brown, M., and Bancroft, F. W. (1935) Amer. J. Med. Sc. *190*, 501.

Quist, A. (1943) Ugeskrift f. Læger *105*, 629.

Rabinowitch, I., and Pines, B. (1943) Surgery *14*, 669.

Ranzi, E. (1908) Arch. f. klin. Chir. *87*, 380.

—» —, and Huber, P. (1935) Wien. klin. Wochenschr. *48*, 289.

Ravdin, I. S. (1941) Amer. J. Med. Sc. *201*, 299.

Reed, C. I., and Lamson, R. W. (1927) J. Immunol. *13*, 433.

Reed, C. I. (1930) J. Immunol. *18*, 181; (1928/29) J. Lab. Clin. Med. *14*, 243.

Reichel, H. (1936) Die Blutkörperchensenkung. (Spinger) Wien.

Reimann-Hunziker, R., and G. (1942) Klin. Wochenschr. *21*, 255.

Reinert, M., and Winterstein, A. (1939) Arch. internat. de pharmacodyn et de thérap. *62*, 47.

Renvall, E. (1945) Nord. Med. *26*, 1195.

Reynolds, J. T., and Jirka, F. J. (1944) Surgery *16*, 485.

Rigdon, R. H., and Wilson, H. (1941) Arch. of Surg. *43*, 64.

Rigdon, R. H., and Schrantz, F. S. (1942) Ann. of Surg. *116*, 122.

Roberts, W. L. (1938) Summaries of doctoral dissertations 1936—37, Madison *2*, 204.

Robertson, H. E. (1938) Amer. J. Surg. N. S. *41*, 3.

Roderick, L. M. (1929) J. Amer. Vet. Med. Ass. *74*, 314; (1931) Amer. J. Physiol. *96*, 413.

—»—, and Schalk, A. F. (1931) North Dakota Agr. Exp. Stat. Bull. 250.

Roholm, K. (1937 a) Hospitalstid. *80*, 2; (1937 b) Dansk Med. Selsk. Forhandl., 23.

Rojak, S. (1939) Inauguraldissertation, Bern.

Rosengren, B., and Stenström, S. (1942) Acta Ophthalmol. *20*, 145.

Rosenqvist, H. (1941) Acta Med. Scand. *107*, 161.

Rosenthal, C. M., and Guzek, J. T. (1943) Arch. of Ophthalmol. *30*, 232.

Rourke, D. M., and Plass, E. D. (1928) J. Clin. Invest. *5*, 531; (1929) Ibid. *7*, 365.

Rous, P., Gilding, H., and Smith, F. (1930) J. Exp. Med. *51*, 807.

Rowntree, L. G., and Shionoya, T. (1927) J. Exp. Med. *46*, 7.

Rudberg, H. (1942) Sv. Läkartidn. *39*, 962.

Rupp, A. (1921) Arch. f. klin. Chir. *115*, 672.

Rychener, R. O. (1942) Southern Med. J. *35*, 652.

Rössle, R. (1937) Virchows Arch. *300*, 180.

Sack, G. (1940) Klin. Wochenschr. *19*, 280.

Sandblom, P. (1944) Acta Chir. Scand. *90*, Suppl. 89.

Dos Santos, J. C. (1938) J. Internat. de Chir. *3*, 625.

Sappington, S. W. (1939) J. Amer. Med. Ass. *113*, 22.

—»—, and Gillis, L. M. (1941) Amer. J. Clin. Path. *11*, 83.

Schaanning, G. (1924) Norsk Mag. f. Lægevidensk. *85*, 505.

Schall, Le Roy A. (1941) J. Amer. Med. Ass. *117*, 581.
Scheidegger, W. (1928) Schweiz. med. Wochenschr. *58*, 78.
Schmidt, A. (1872) Pflügers Arch. *6*, 445.
—»— (1892) Zur Blutlehre. Leipzig.
Schmidt, L. H. (1935) J. Biol. Chem. *109*, 449.
Schmidt-Mühlheim, A. (1880) Du Bois-Reymond Arch. f. Physiol. 33.
Schmitz, A. (1935) Z. physiol. Chem. *234*, 216.
Schofield, F. S. (1922) Canad. Vet. Rec. *3*, 74; (1923—24) J. Amer. Vet. Med. Ass. *64*, 553.
Schütz, F. (1941) Quarterly J. of Pharm. and Pharmacol. *14*, 45.
Schäffer, W. P. (1935) Wien. klin. Wochenschr. *48*, 1265.
Sedwitz, S. H. (1942) Amer. Heart J. *24*, 774.
—»—, and Baker, E. C. (1944) Amer. J. Surg. *103*, 105.
Seegers, W. H., Warner, E. D., Brinkhous, K. M., and Smith, H. P. (1942) Science *96*, 300.
Seegers, W. H., and Smith, H. P. (1943) Proc. Soc. Exp. Biol. Med. *52*, 159.
Shionoya, T. (1927) J. Exp. Med. *46*, 19.
Shlevin, E. L., and Lederer, M. (1944) Ann. Int. Med. *21*, 332.
Silfverskiöld, B. P. (1940) Skand. Arch. f. Physiol. *83*, 175.
Simon, L. (1943) Acta Obst. Gyn. *23*, 570.
Simpson, K. (1940) Lancet *2*, 744.
Singer, B. (1929) Deutsch. Arch. f. klin. Med. ref. *164*; 2, 175.
Sköld, E. (1936 a) Acta Med. Scand. *88*, 450; (1936 b) Nord. Med. Tidskr. *12*, 1659; (1937) Ibid. *13*, 998.
—»— (1944) On haemophilia in Sweden. Acta Med. Scand. Suppl. 150.
Soda, T., and Egami, F. (1938) Bull. of Chem. Soc. Japan *13*, 652.
Solandt, D. Y., and Best, C. H. (1938) Lancet *2*, 130.
Solomon, H. A. (1941) New York State J. Med. *41*, 45.
Sperry, W. M., and Schoenheimer, R. (1935) J. Biol. Chem. *110*, 655.
Spiro, K., and Fuld, E. (1904) Hofmeisters Beiträge *6*, 171.
Stahmann, M. A., Heubner, C. F., and Link, K. P. (1941) J. Biol. Chem. *138*, 513.
Stansfield, F. R. (1942) Brit. Med. J. April 4th, 436.
Starr, A., Frank, H. A., and Fine, J. (1942) J. Amer. Med. Ass. *118*, 1192.

Stewart, J. D. and Rourke, G. M. (1940) J. Clin. Invest. *19*, 695.
Ström, J. (1938) Acta Med. Scand. *96*, 365.
Strömbeck, J. P. (1942) Nord. Med. *13*, 522.
Stuber, B., and Lang, K. (1930) Arch. f. exp. Path. u. Pharm. *154*, 22.
de Takats, G. (1943) Surg. Gyn. Obst. *77*, 31.
—»—, Surg, M., and Fowler, E. F. (1945) Surgery *17*, 153.
Thornton, T. F., Adam, W. E., and Carlton, L. M. (1945) Surgery *18*, 595.
Thorsén, G. (1942) Nord. Med. *16*, 3347; (1945 a) Nord. Med. *27*, 1553; (1945 b) Arch. Physic. Med. *26*, 638.
Vance, B. M. (1934) Amer. J. Surg. *26*, 19.
Vannfält, K. A. (1940) Acta Tuberc. Scand. *14*, 37.
Vartiainen, A. and I. (1929) Acta Soc. Med. Fennicae Ser. A XIII Fasc. I.
Vincke, E., and Oelkers, H. A. (1937) Arch. f. exp. Path. u. Pharm. *187*, 594.
Vincke, E., and Never, H. E. (1940) Arch. f. exp. Path. u. Pharm. *194*, 308.
Veal, J. R., and Hussey, H. H. (1945) Surgery *17*, 218.
Virchow, R. (1846) Beitr. z. exp. Path. *2*, 227.
Wadsworth, A., Maltaner, F., and E. (1937) Am. J. Physiol. *119*, 80.
Wakim, K. G., and Gatch, W. D. (1943) Surg. Obstetr. Gyn. *76*, 655.
Walker, J. (1945) Surgery *17*, 54.
—»—, and Rhoads, J. E. (1944) Surgery *15*, 859.
Warburg, E. (1942) Nord. Med. *16*, 2841.
Wassén, E., and Zander, G. (1945) Sv. Läkartidn. *42*, 1768.
Wassén, E., Fogstrand, I., and Masreliez, N. (1945) Sv. Läkartidn. *42*, 2926.
Waters, E. T., Markowitz, J., and Jaques, L. B. (1938) Science *87*, 582.
Welch, C. E., Faxon, M. H., and McGahey, C. E. (1942) Surgery *12*, 163.
Westerborn, A. (1946) Nord. Med. *29*, 347.
Westergren, A. (1920) Acta Med. Scand. *54*, 247.
—»— (1937) Nord. Med. Tidskr. *13*, 913; (1938) *15*, 837.
Wetterdal, P. (1941 a) Acta Med. Scand. *107*, 123; (1941 b) Z. f. Gynäkol. *65*, 173..
—»— (1942) Acta Obst. Gyn. Scand. *22*, Suppl. 2.

Widström, G., and Wilander, O. (1936) Acta Med. Scand. 88, 434.

Wiesenfled, I. H., and Phillips, E. .(1944) Arch. of Otolaryngol. 40, 497.

Wilander, O. (1938 a) Skand. Arch. f. Physiol. 81, Suppl. XV; (1938 b) Acta Med. Scand. 94, 258.

Williams, O. B., and van de Carr, F. R. (1927) Proc. Soc. Exp. Biol. Med. 24, 798.

—»— (1928) J. Immunol. 15, 13.

Willners, G. (1942) Nord. Med. 16, 3374.

Wising, P. (1937) Acta Med. Scand. 91, 550; (1938) 94, 506.

Witts, L. J. (1940) Brit. Med. J. 1, 484.

Wolfrom, M. L., and McNeely, W. H. (1945) J. Amer. Chem. Soc. 67, 748.

Wolfrom, M. L., and Karabinos, J. V. (1945) J. Amer. Chem. Soc. 67, 679.

—»—, Smith, C. S., Ohliger, P. H., Lee, J., and Keller, O. (1945) J. Amer. Chem. Soc. 67, 1624.

Wolfrom, M. L., Weisblat, D. I., Karabinos, J. V., McNeely, W. H., and McLean, J. (1943) J. Amer. Chem. Soc. 65, 2077.

Wolfrom, M. L., and Rice, F. A. H. (1946) J. Am. Chem. Soc. 68, 532.

Wright, I., and Prandoni, A. (1942) J. Amer. Med. Ass. 120, 1015.

Wulff, H. (1942) Nord. Med. 16, 2840.

Wöhlisch, E. (1929) Ergebn. d. Physiol. 28, 443.

Zakrzewski, Z. (1932 a) Z. f. Krebsforsch. 36, 513; (1932 b) Arch. f. exp. Zellforsch. 13, 152.

—»— (1933) Klin. Wochenschr. 11, 113.

Zilliacus, H. (1945) Sv. Läkartidn. 42, 2625.

—»— (1946 a) Acta Med. Scand. Suppl. 171; (1946 b) Nord. Med. 29, 277.

Zimmerman, L. M., and de Takats, G. (1931) Arch. Surg. 23, 937.

Zuckerkandl, F., and Meissner-Klebermass, L. (1931) Biochem. Z. 236, 19.

Zunz, E. (1935) Sang. 9, 1, 124; (1934) C. r. Soc. Biol. 116, 336.

—»— (1934) Bull. Ac. R. de Méd. Belg. Sér. 5. 14, 537.

von Zweigbergk, J. O. (1942) Nord. Med. 16, 3089.

Øllgaard, E. (1943 a) Klin. Wochenschr. 22, 80; (1943 b) Acta Med. Scand. 115, 1.

Östner, K. (1942) Acta Med. Scand. Suppl. 127.

Index.